1975

book may be kept

FOURTEEN DAYS

*Whatever You Do,* DON'T PANIC

*Whatever You Do,* **DON'T PANIC**

*by* JEAN MERCIER

*Illustrated by* JOHN HUEHNERGARTH

*Doubleday & Company, Inc., Garden City, New York*

All of the characters in this book
are fictitious, and any resemblance
to actual persons, living or dead,
is purely coincidental.

*For my friends.*

*Whatever You Do,* DON'T PANIC

## 1

Like one coming out of an anesthetic, slowly, I found myself, on a morning in early March, gazing out of the kitchen window. It wasn't unusual for me to find myself waking up in the kitchen—that's the way all my days began, then. I could hardly remember ever getting out of bed during the three months that we had lived in Catatonia, a suburb surrounded by suburbs some fifty miles from New York.

Knowing that my husband would be streaking through the kitchen at any moment, looking for a cup of coffee

WHATEVER YOU DO, DON'T PANIC

to bolt, I wrenched my attention to the stove and, by dint of infinite practice, stood at the ready when he arrived. He grabbed the steaming cup from my hand and muttered, "Thanks, Mama" (I think that's what he muttered). After one gulp, he was gone; he was in the car, gliding down the long hill on the first relay of his daily race with the train.

I let my sagging body slip down to the floor and sat there, refusing to face the tasks of the day. Sipping my coffee lovingly and slowly, I thought for the thousandth time how delicious it would be if I might be awakened by a gentle hand, holding a cup of absolutely perfect coffee. A cup of coffee in bed! Not a mink coat. Not a swimming pool. Not even a Goya or a First Folio. Just to be cherished enough by someone who would give me a cup of coffee in bed. After a few minutes, I started to wish for something else, equally impossible: that the view from the kitchen window was the dear, familiar, reassuring side of an apartment building in New York; not naked trees, stone walls, and little fur-bearing animals darting about. And that I didn't awaken every morning in a silence so deep it made me fear I had become deaf in the night.

Then my better, nobler self started picking on me. It was almost seven-fifteen and I knew that I should stop ducking the inevitable and rouse our three small daughters.

But no. Not yet. Sitting on the floor, I tried to remember why we had ever thought it would be a good idea to move to the country. The little hut we had bought stood on a high hill at the very edge of a fine sweep of trees, cat briars, and poison ivy. One interesting architectural feature of the house was that the front door opened directly upon a view of the bathroom. Full face. We really must have been exhausted by the long search for a house when we fell for this. My senses reeled when I thought of how much we had paid for it; rather, had promised to pay for it. But in writing. That was the trouble. The promise was in writing.

Other than the front door with the view of the bathroom, the house consisted of a closet-sized living room, a dining room, a kitchen, and two tiny bedrooms; all on one floor, but separated by three or four stairs from each other. It was a split-level house, in the loosest possible sense of the word; "shattered"-level would be more like it. There was no attic or basement, but there was a garage on a lower level that we had put to use as a basement; we needed the room more than the car did.

It wasn't so much that there were so few rooms—it was that they each looked like half a room. And since the house was, as I said, on the very edge of the two-acre lot, I suspected that the builder had planned to put several more such half-houses on the land; that we were, in short, a case of arrested development.

We had a second floor, unfinished, and this space was to provide three bedrooms and a bath for the children. Hank and I expected to make these rooms ourselves, when we could afford the time and materials. I had discovered the origin of "do-it-yourself"—it was not a

11

decision, it was a command. You called people and asked them to do a job for you and they said, "Do it yourself."

To be fair, the house hadn't seemed so small before it was filled with our furniture. And Hank had been charmed by the high hill on which it sat, and the fact that there were no other houses close by.

"Boy," I said to myself. "That was some Christmas party."

The Christmas party comes in because that's where I met Hank. I was working at a model agency in New York, and my employer had sternly invited me to the agency's Yuletide function. I did my best, nodding and smiling and dodging around, and eventually became aware of a quiet, pleasant gentleman who (I made sure) became aware of me. When we were introduced and fell into conversation, we discovered that we both had listened avidly to a radio program (sponsored by the old Majestic Radio Company) of the thirties. David Ross used to open the program, as only he could, with: "Drifting sands and a caravan, the desert's endless space; lustrous eyes 'neath Eastern skies, and a woman's veil—ed face." Even now, I can still hear the voice of the male lead, saying: "You will soon become my wife, Myra. My—*Arabian*—wife," though I can't remember much else about it.

With a bond like that, and others equally strong, there was nothing else for us to do but get married. When Hank asked me, I said, "Yes—when?" with a quick coylessness that might have daunted a lesser man. It was all I wanted, marriage; I'm one of those ambitionless, ignorant, spineless women who lean to the radical theory that woman's place is in the home—washing, cooking, mending: stuff like that. *But not here.* In our spacious, economical apartment; our nice brownstone in Manhattan, where Hank could sleep until eight o'clock, have a good breakfast, and walk to work, instead of racing off in the middle of the night, with one sip of scalding coffee to sustain him!

During the seven years that we had lived there, life had gone along like a song, to hear me tell it. I had all I wanted: Hank, and our children, and I was living where I could understand things, in the city. New York was home to me in the way it can be only to those who are born elsewhere. Grover Whalen isn't in it with us. Like millions before and after me, I fell in love with Manhattan at first sight, as soon as I arrived there from Cleveland, Ohio. And even in Cleveland, I had never ventured anywhere so rural that there were no sidewalks underfoot. "So what am I doing *here?*" I thought. "It's against all nature!" The root of the problem was that *I* was against all nature; at least, the idea of living in the middle of it.

I wished I could blame somebody else for what I was convinced was the one rash move of our lives. True, it was Hank who had insisted it was time to buy a house— but I didn't say no. Partial as I am to our girls, I was easily taken in by Hank's arguments that they needed more living space, lots of fresh, clean, healthy air, and good schools. We started looking at houses, and the closer they were to New York, the more things Hank found

13

wrong with them. Such as price. Finally we had come to this—pretty pass? Yes. If I believed in naming estates, that's what I would paint on the mailbox, "PRETTY PASS." "Either that," I said, "or 'ABANDON HOPE ALL YE WHO——'"

"Stop that!" I said. "That's going too far!" I told myself to stop feeling sorry for myself and to get up and do something constructive. We can't all be Mrs. America, though. I, for one, needed a little more time to wake up. You see, among other things, I was afraid of the dark in Catatonia—the dark with its bizarre silence that was merely italicized by what sounds there were. (Like those darned things that chirped all night—"peepers," the children called them. I knew they were peepers all right, but what kind, I wondered. Queer birds, that didn't know they were supposed to be famous for going to sleep early.) I fought sleep to the death every night. By the time I dozed off, it was time to get up. That's why it took me so long to get going. I alternated between being nervous as a tap dancer, and being completely dazed.

"*Get them up.* Look. It's nearly seven-thirty. Maybe if you get them up now, they'll go to sleep before midnight tonight." But being alone was too healing to be disturbed. I had to regain my strength, all of it, because all the children were going to be home, all day. The two older girls had spent two days in school here in the fresh, clean, healthy air, and had promptly caught a cold which they were presently passing around like a loving cup.

Our girls are the most beautiful, the most interesting,

15

the most beguiling, the sweetest, and the nicest children I have ever known. They are also the loudest, most infuriating, most irritating human beings on earth. Living with them is like being caught forever at a brawl where you are the only person sober, and which you can't leave because the man who brought you won't hear of it, and you don't have carfare. But dear children. They ask permission before stealing a piece of candy, they are interested in everything from flowers to space travel, and they are liked not only by our friends but also by our enemies, and even by other *mothers*.

I resolved, as I do every morning, and every night when I lie awake in a torment of remorse, that I was not going to lose my temper today. I was not going to yell, or smack a small behind. But I knew that within an hour after I greeted all three with a loving kiss, I would be putting the toughest Marine drill instructor to shame. There are some mothers I know who, when they find their patience running out, head for a bedroom and stick their heads under a pillow, to keep from exploding and damaging their children's psyches. But I can never make it to the pillow on time.

I was shocked into the final stages of wakefulness as, with a scream and a leap into the air, I responded to the entrance of our middle daughter, Jennie. She had fallen down three steps, and had managed, in some esoteric fashion, to knock over three chairs, none of which was any closer than six feet to her line of flight. Jennie's large, blue eyes looked anxiously into mine, which looked back just as anxiously. She was afraid I would be

16

vehement about the racket; I was afraid she was hurt. She never is. Sometimes I think she is more sponge rubber than flesh and bones. Each of us decided at the same time that there was no cause for alarm and we smiled and kissed good morning.

With Jennie, my tolerance stretches farther than with Louise, from force of habit. Jennie was born only one year later than Louise, and since Louise was so young, she had to be taught to share—clothes, toys, parental affection, everything. I accomplished this teaching in the only way I knew how. I got into the fights between them on the losing side.

I remembered a time when Jennie was learning to walk, at nine months, and had happened to get into Louise's way. Louise had tried to remove the obstacle from her path by the simple expedient of lifting Jennie up by the neck. With an outraged roar, I had leaped to Jennie's rescue and had had quite a bit to say to Louise, winding up the sermon by demanding that Louise never do such a thing again, and that she apologize. Her apology was, "I'm sorry, Jennie; I didn't know it was you."

Anyway, if my method of settling quarrels between them was a little less than orthodox, or even wise, it had worked, because the girls had grown to be fast friends.

I set out Jennie's favorite breakfast, a substance that I regard as sawdust but which she loves. I indulge the preference because it says on the box it will provide every possible nutriment for this and every other day.

Just then, Louise joined us. She entered very seriously, having come from a book as usual, and began talking about a situation that had aroused her scorn. "This man outside the castle says, 'Let down your hair.' She does, and he climbs up all the way on it! CAN YOU IMAGINE HOW THAT WOULD HURT?" Jennie was properly indignant at the hoax, and they both discussed the sort of thing that is written these days, and how careful you have to be not to believe everything you read.

Listening to them, I thought of how much at a disadvantage I was. The girls are much smarter than I, and I know it. The only time I came even close to getting a bit of my own back was before Louise started going to school, when I casually mentioned that I could spell. Louise gazed at me suspiciously and said: "How do you spell 'horse'?" I spoke the letters offhandedly, as if spelling aloud was one of the ways I used to break hearts, and for the rest of the day both girls were very respectful.

I left the two to their breakfast and took the several steps (about ten) that brought me from the kitchen through the dining and living rooms to the "master" bedroom, wondering what the architect of this house would have designed for slave quarters. By turning sideways, I could inch my way between the bed and the cot where three-year-old Miranda lay, still sleeping. Tenderly, I gathered her up and reverse-inched my way to a rocker that was wedged into a corner. Although you couldn't rock in the rocker, you could sit in it. I sat holding Miranda and immediately started feeling better, as I thought about her and the other two.

18

At first glance it might seem that the girls are very
like; this is an illusion caused by their all having straight,
wheat-colored hair. (As a matter of fact, they very often
seem to be peeping through sheaves of wheat, because
the dime stores refuse to sell barrettes, bobby pins, or
any other device that will stay in the hair of a small
girl.) Actually, they are not alike at all. Louise's eyes
are green-tea-colored. They are very wide eyes, set far
apart, and they are tipped suddenly at the ends, so that
she has a slightly Oriental look. She comes so close to
formal beauty that she would be uninteresting, except
for her eyes and the impression she gives of always being
poised for flight, ready to take wing. Louise swallows
books whole, she can ride a horse, she can sing on key,
she knows what Secretary Benson could have done (but
is too polite to suggest what he *should* have done); she
is deft, she is adroit, she is brilliant, she is good. She
is unaffected and natural except when under the spell
of literature, and at those times, she sounds as if she
were reading aloud—as in a conversation I once overheard between her and a playmate: "What started out
to be a pleasant afternoon has ended in tragedy. It has
developed that my mother made plans which will not
allow of our keeping our appointment. Sadly, you will
have to have the game of jacks without me." I think
that her habit of referring to waifs as "little ragged
muffins," and such slips as "woman's intooshun" are due
to her too-rapid perusal of the printed page. Sometimes
I worry about how she is going to earn a living, because
I believe there is no field in which one is paid for reading

to oneself, and this is all Louise really wants to do. At other times, though, I am sure that if I walked out for good tomorrow (a course which tempts me, often), Louise would take over and run things better than I do. You may say that wouldn't be too hard. But Louise is only six.

Then there is Jennie, in the middle. She is a laugher, round and blue of eye. She is as beautiful and talented as Louise but in a different way. With Louise, she can discuss such infantile matters as the number of light years to the moon, that there is little gravity there, the best way to insure world peace, and what is wrong with the guided missile program. But she is too gay to spend much thought on these problems—she is a droll child, who always seems to be peeking at you over the top of a mushroom. She is an elf, a sprite, who can, nonetheless, tear a blanket. Could Bronco Horvath do that, I wondered? Or could Archie Moore or Floyd Patterson tear a blanket—not an old, weak, worn blanket: a brand-new, strong, virgin-wool blanket with a six-inch nylon binding? Jennie's slip shows, her shoelaces are always tripping her, her hems invariably part company with her dresses. Jennie it is who unmasks me by saying, when we have guests and she sees lighted candles on the dining-room table: "Oh goody! Is there going to be another hurricane?"—just when, of course, I am trying to behave as if we ate by candlelight all the time. Jennie it is who joyfully shouts to lady guests that she has a doll who *also* wears blue eye shadow. Jennie lives at the top of her lungs and my nervous system, and just as surely at the top of her heart, or wherever it is that love is. She cares.

And Miranda, this child in my arms, was the baby. She was the only baby I had had who knew how to be a baby. *She* had cuddled. Now at three-going-on-four, she was as full of authority and simplicity, as wise and as sweet as a poem by Emily Dickinson. And just about as short, too. Short or not, the entire family was in captivity to her. We invariably did as she suggested, because she was always right. She had a way of making the world understand, clearly, that there were certain things that were seemly and correct; others, absolutely inadmissible in the proper scheme of things. This would be intolerable, except that she was enchanting. It was with a pang that I realized, sitting there with her, that I shouldn't have called her "Our Glorious Leader" as I had in a recent, impatient moment. I was ashamed because she had accepted the title as her just due. And I was apprehensive about how she would look at me when she learned the facts about the original Glorious Leader.

The only way I can truly sum up the girls is to say that if you substituted a safety pin for a button on Louise's clothing, she would never notice it, and neither would anyone else, because people looking at her rarely got past her eyes. Jennie would notice the pin, and she would care, but she would be too good-natured to complain. As for Miranda, she would look at you if there was a button missing from anything of hers and you

21

would sew the *right* button on forthwith; what's more, with matching thread.

There in the rocking chair, the number of times the floors had been bathed in milk, the mud on the carpets, the lost mittens, the works of art that adorn our walls, the torn dresses, and the overdue library books seemed unimportant.

Then, our quiet corner was invaded by what sounded like the entire Green Bay Packers team, somehow contained in the slight, fragile bodies of two girls who, between them, weighed no more than seventy pounds. Miranda jumped awake and out of my arms to return their loving screeches. I permitted them to become reacquainted in their own inimitable way for about ten minutes, then found myself falling into my familiar, affectionate prose: "Unless you want to gain fame as the only gray-haired children in the world, get dressed, brush your teeth, and tidy your room, right now!" This was a mistake. Instead of scaring them, I had aroused their intellectual curiosity, and I had a difficult time avoiding a seminar on the effects of fright on the human system, explaining why a person's hair could turn white with fright overnight.

## 2

After giving Miranda her breakfast, I pondered the problem—for about half an hour, maybe more, maybe less—of a suitable outfit for the serious housecleaning I planned for the day. The all-inclusive gray dampness of the wintry morning made me shiver, so the ensemble I finally put together consisted of one white and one blue sock (discards of Hank's, saved in the wistful hope that the mates would someday show up), a pair of blue jeans with a dejected seat, grimy sneakers, and one of Hank's shirts that had had its collar turned for the last

23

time. Gazing at my reflection in the living-room mirror, I said: "Good morning, Mrs. Lamont. Was your mother, by any chance, frightened by a Swirl?"

I stared a moment longer, then started humming "The Jersey Bounce" and broke into the jitterbug solo demanded by the costume. Then, in the midst of a new step I had just invented, I suddenly became aware of a pair of watchful adult eyes. There at the window stood Norma Beige, president of the PTA, the League of Women Voters, the Mothers' March, the Cancer Crusade, the Catatonia Women's Club, the Republican Club of Catatonia, the Democratic Club of Catatonia, and just about everything fit to be presided over.

With a cry of dismay I ran to the door and admitted Mrs. Beige, resisting with some effort the impulse to curtsy and yank my forelock. "Good morning," Mrs. Beige said. "I hope it is not too early to call. The fact is that I was on my way to school and decided to stop by since you were on the way." Each word came from her lips in a mesmerizing cadence. Each word was given its full due and no more. It was as though she were an impartial judge—fair, but absolutely implacable.

"Oh, of course not!" I cried gaily, "honestly, I wasn't doing a thing; I—won't you sit down?"

At that moment the girls came in, still in their nightgowns. I tried to see us through Mrs. Beige's eyes, and quickly decided that I would rather not. I got the girls back to their room, mostly by dragging, and returned to my guest. While one part of my mind was trying to figure out the reason for this unexpected visit, dancing

24

with visions of being asked to head the Hostess Committee, or play the lead in the big fund-raising play,
or edit the school bulletin, another and more active part
of my mind was busy wondering at the "presence" of this
woman—"presence" as the term is used in the theatre.
Such was her dignity that she escaped looking ridiculous
even in the Catatonia uniform for winter: woolen Bermuda shorts and knee-length woolen socks, chukkas, and
an enormous sweater. Her hair was so short as to be
almost crew-cut, in the prescribed fashion. She should
have been wearing one of those Peck & Peck hound's-
tooth-check suit, hat, and topcoat ensembles, Enna
Jetticks, and heavy-gauge nylons. In any other clime, she
certainly would have been.

I offered a cigarette and coffee, but both offers were
declined graciously. Then, as I was trying to think of
what to say next, Mrs. Beige said she would be glad
of a cup of tea, with cream please, if there was any
handy. "Of course, of course," I said. "No trouble at all."
I stumbled into the kitchen, devoutly hoping that someplace or other there might be a stray tea bag left over
from the last time Hank or I had been sick. After a frantic
search, I finally reappeared with a steaming pot, scalding
myself and further staining the rug. I presented it to Mrs.
Beige with the shy admission that the cream seemed to
be all gone, adding that I hoped homogenized milk
would be all right.

After a long silence, while I tried to keep my feet still
and pretended not to notice that the two older girls were
tittering and eavesdropping just out of sight, but most of

all hoping prayerfully that someone wouldn't push someone else and launch one of those brannigans that add
such zest to our lives—after a long silence, while Mrs.
Beige slowly sipped her tea as though both she and I
had all the time in the world and I thought that
"presence" or not, sitting as though you were playing a
cello, which she was, without a cello, was an awful way
for a woman to sit, she finally broached the subject of
her call. Her judicial manner of speaking persisted. Once
again each word was given its just, proper desert.

"Mrs. Lamont comma you have been here for three
months and have presumably had a chance to settle in
period new sentence While we know comma that you
do have a pre-school child and that you cannot perhaps
do all you would like to assist Your PTA comma we are
sure you can do your fair share along with many other
mothers in your situation period new paragraph Now we
note on the questionnaire you filled out that you express
an interest in writing comma drama comma and the work
of the hospitality committee period Our Board has
forwarded this information to the Chairmen of these
Committees comma and you will hear from them officially
in a day or two period But the purpose of my visit comma
was to say that we would be pleased to have you assist
in typing stencils semi-colon and that your help would
be welcome in mending costumes for the play and also
in helping wash up the coffee cups and ash trays after
our regular meetings period"

When she finally left—with my cries of delight at
being so honored and my assurances of complete co-

john huehnergarth

operation ringing in her ears—so dashed was my ego, so stunned was I by my failure to present myself to Those Who Ran Things as a wise, witty, capable woman of affairs (of such stuff as Chairmen and even Presidents are made)—that I dragged from the kitchen to the bedrooms for over an hour, trying as unsuccessfully as Hamlet to decide between doing the dishes or making the beds. I realized that Hamlet was faced with an entirely different problem, but his agony could have been no greater. The most that was accomplished was adding Mrs. Beige's tray to the dish pile, and by means of repeated threats, on an ascending scale, seeing that the girls dressed themselves, after a fashion.

I was saved from making the decision as the phone rang, and the girls were upon me instantly. Here's a household hint: if you can't find your children, and get tired of calling them, pick up the phone. No matter if your children are at the movies, in school, visiting their grandmother, or on a field trip in some distant city, they will be upon you magically within seconds after you pick up the phone.

Jennie and Miranda twined themselves around me, murmuring endearments. Louise climbed onto a stool and clutched the hand with which I was trying to hold the phone, claiming my immediate attention on grounds of extreme emergency. Somehow managing to get out a cool, poised, "Won't you hold on a second, please," I covered up the mouthpiece, and with more warmth and less poise, gave a quick lecture on crime and punishment, mostly the latter, including Devil's Island and the remoter reaches of Siberia. I promised to illustrate the lecture, if they so much as *breathed* till after the call was completed.

Speaking into the phone again and recognizing the caller, I resumed my everyday voice. Soon we were deep in a conversation that was interrupted many times by little things like Jennie's holding her breath and pretending to black out, Miranda's dumping the contents of the sugar bowl on the table, and various screeches, thuds, and giggles. Under the circumstances, I had difficulty keeping up with the conversation on the phone, but when I hung up I was reasonably certain that Francesca had wanted to remind me of our town meeting the next evening, and how important it was that Hank and I be there.

I discovered that the girls had shrewdly vacated the kitchen, and were playing quietly in the living room. It seemed that I would be the gainer if I accepted the peace and quiet, instead of carrying out my threats.

Resolving to get something done, I started in on the dishes. No. I'm not saying it right. What I meant to say was that I started to start in on the dishes by gathering them all together in the kitchen sink. They looked so formidable, however, so *demanding*, that I found myself staring at them in dismay and starting to woolgather again, this time about Francesca and her husband. How about them, I thought.

Francesca and Herbert were among the few people we knew in Catatonia. We didn't even know them till about a month after we moved—at that time, they had called on us, after I met Fran at a PTA meeting, and had taken us in hand socially. They had been kind to us and we were indebted to them for one or two pleasant dinners, and for information as to where to shop, which dentist, doctor, plumber, and sitter to call (not that there was much of a choice, since Catatonia was just a village; the yellow pages of the telephone book were amazingly thin).

They were "personalities." Herb, an expert on narrow ties, thin lapels, and swatches, was men's fashion editor of *Parvenu*, the weekly magazine with the tremendous circulation. Fran and he had met about two years after she had arrived in Manhattan from Nebraska, or was it Wyoming? She was the daughter and sole heiress of either a cattle baron or an oil millionaire and, having arrived in New York with a big bank roll, became a dabbler in various fields. She patronized Greenwich Village artists for awhile, then put some money into a Broadway show which was successful (terrible, but successful). It was during her "writing" period that she and Herb met and decided that they were in love. They were married at a lavish ceremony which was duly recorded in *Parvenu* and all other magazines and newspapers, and then they honeymooned in Bermuda. No, not Bermuda. Bermuda was not in style that year. They had honeymooned in Rome; everyone was very high on Rome that year.

They had bought their house in Catatonia after investigating all the regions of suburbia surrounding New York; they had chosen Catatonia because of its reputation for excellent schools, beaches, and abundance of names.

"You are bound to get involved with people when you

have children," Fran had told me at our first meeting, "so it is good to know that those with whom you get involved are not just dreary little housewives and dull husbands, but People Who Do Things."

I admired their easy way of doing things but I couldn't escape an uneasiness at their way of *always* doing the *right* things. Their house was a centuries-old Colonial which they had had restored (guided by an eminent architect) and updated, and added on to. It had a gourmet's corner (instead of a kitchen), a breakfast room, a luncheon room, a dining room, a sitting room, a room for standing up, a party room, dressing rooms for everybody, even a room for mud. It was all set up so there would be no dust anywhere and so that their children would color in the coloring room, paint in the painting room, play with blocks in the block house, and do all the other things in the proper rooms at exactly the right time. Their two boys were "well adjusted" and, like their parents, always did the right thing at the right time and damn the consequences.

Francesca and Herbert considered themselves violently nonconformist and showed the world they were by filling their Colonial house with contemporary furniture and paintings and other art objects (expensive, but not necessarily valuable, contemporary things). Fran flaunted her independence by rebelling against the Catatonia uniform of Bermuda shorts and knee-length socks by wearing Bermuda shorts and knee-length socks in *color;* bright pinks and plaids and vivid stripes. Sometimes she even wore the uniform in solid, unrelieved black, and with her blonde hair cut so closely, wearing this uniform, she strongly resembled a member of the SS.

No one could dislike them, I thought. Sometimes, though, they did not seem quite human. It seemed, indeed, that their house was not so much a home, but rather a perfect stage set, and that they were actors who had been handed fat roles in a successful play, and had talent enough to fill the roles competently, with nice understatement. Practically the only enthusiasm they showed was when they were discussing "names"; even brand names. You should hear the reverence in Fran's voice when she said "Baccarat" or "Steuben" or "Madame Alexander." She always let it be known that there was wine in the pot roast or that the chicken had been marinated in brandy, and that Koussevitzky's second cousin was an intimate of theirs.

I wouldn't have wasted time puzzling over this couple were it not for my fear that all the other inhabitants of Catatonia were equally unreal. I couldn't feel at home among them. Besides Francesca, there was Blanche. Francesca was pleasant and charming, but Blanche was sweet. Yes, Blanche was very, very sweet—being in her company was like being drowned in warm, melted marshmallows. I had once been a witness when Blanche had smiled and said with only minimum ruefulness, "Oh, my soufflé has collapsed." *Anyone* knows how a real, red-blooded woman would react to such a catastrophe! If Blanche had been honest, she would have yelled, slammed at least a couple of doors, and thrown a few little, value-less things. But dear me, no; not Blanche.

32

After five minutes with Blanche, one might welcome the astringency of Grazie, who was a sort of Gwen Cafritz to Francesca's Perle Mesta. Francesca and Grazie were habitual committee chairmen and they usually managed to be elected co-chairmen, equal bosses, of whatever PTA or civic project was being launched. They were inseparable, not because they were fond of each other, but because they wanted to keep an eye on each other, as they were keen rivals for social leadership. Grazie was mean: quietly mean, and bitterly, unfunnily sarcastic. She it was who had looked to see if I was wearing shoes upon learning that I couldn't drive. Grazie had a small, slick head and her hair and skin were the color of golden toast. She lived in an ultra-modern house whose decoration, appointments, paint, and even pets were chosen to complement her coloring; the pets were a couple of Siamese cats. Her uniform was of rich, raw silk, in a shade which matched her hair, skin, housepaint, and cats, and since she was so thin as to be almost shapeless, she rather resembled a frozen fish stick.

The husbands of these women and others I had met in Catatonia were distinguished only in that they were, to me at least, indistinguishable. I couldn't tell one from the other. Like Herbert, they were all in communications: radio, television, magazines, and advertising. One or two were writers of books; all were fellows of finite charm. Each had developed a hair-trigger chuckle and the habit of saying "zounds!" in deference to country-squirehood. I never thought I'd live to hear people chuckle and say "zounds!" in real life. I wouldn't have missed it for anything. They were "sincere"—men of the too-hearty handclasp and the urgent smile. These boys acknowledged an introduction to anybody by gently pressing one of his hands in both of theirs, while they gazed, misty-eyed with care, into the eyes of the person they were meeting. Could such unadulterated love, for a total stranger, be credited? They were always leaping to light cigarettes, open car doors, fill plates or glasses, and I mistrusted the whole lot of them to the same degree that I mistrusted bake shops that called themselves "Sanitary Bake Shops."

*"O Pioneers!"* I thought, and wondered what kind of homesteads such odd pioneers would establish in this suburban frontier; pioneers who looked like off-duty gardeners even at parent-teacher conferences and who never called the school principal "Mister." I sighed, thinking that among other things, people here seemed to be those who would have to cut down if they earned less than $85,000 yearly; people who would give their teeth for a chance to get on "Person to Person"; people who thought it was nice to be important, but not important to be nice; who were more ingratiating than gracious, more personalities than persons. In my estimation, they were people who read Daphne du Maurier, and discussed Kafka; well, not *discussed* him exactly, but said, "Kafka!" reverently and raised their eyes, as if they were at a loss to describe how they felt about Kafka, which they were, because they had no opinions about Kafka, not having read Kafka. They were, I felt, people invariably trying to prove not who, but what they

34

were, and trying to determine what, not who, others were.

Becoming aware that it was nearly lunchtime, I brought myself back to the tasks at hand. I made plans for the afternoon—doing the breakfast and luncheon dishes all at once, making the beds, and then maybe painting the kitchen. Then, I remembered that the girls had had a banana for dessert every day for the last week. "BANANAS!" Jennie had shouted each time. "They're not dessert! They're not even food. They're just something you're supposed to put on cereal for breakfast." I dug around and found a mix, and was able to surprise them with a devil's-food cake with chocolate icing. (Sometimes I think you need only one rule for cooking: if you can't put garlic in it, put chocolate in it.)

The cake was received in a stunned silence that was evidence in itself of the dearth of taste thrills Mama had been providing. Then Jennie closed her eyes, stretched forth her arms, and said: "Take my hand, Louise; I'm a stranger in paradise."

## 3

The children made very sure that the cake wouldn't sit around gathering dust, and when they had satisfied themselves that there was no longer any need to fear a blood-sugar deficiency, we sat in the kitchen and chatted for a while. Then, once again, the noise became unbearable—we all talk at once in our house, and what would be, singly, sentences of wit, brilliance, or plain common sense, degenerates into a hideous uproar. Taking advantage of my position as biggest and oldest, I yelled the loudest and demanded that Louise and Jennie do something quiet after lunch, because Miranda had to have a nap and I was going to get some work done, or else! When one of them came forth with the inevitable "or else what?" I lost all patience, and they faded.

By this time, the dishes had reached such proportions that they would have taxed the kitchens of the Waldorf. Deciding that I had been in the kitchen long enough and that it would boost my morale to get out of it, I betook myself to the bedroom to tackle the beds. Halfway there, I stopped short and reminded myself that I really ought to get at the ironing. "There are at least three cartons of clean clothes just aching to be ironed and if you do one more washing," I said to myself, "you'll have to find another box somewhere." Since this made sense to me, I set up the board and, closing my eyes, said "Eeny, meeny, miney, mo," to the three boxes. Then, when I came to "mo," I sang, "It had to be you, wonderful you," realizing that the carton tapped by fate was loaded with organdy pinafores and the fanciest of dresses. "Shall we have another go-round," I mused, "and make it two out of three? They won't need those things for months, if ever." "No," I answered firmly. "They have to be done sooner or later. And the cane you ring is the cane you get."

After fifteen minutes of concentration, I was enchanted by the sight of a prim little dress swinging from a hanger. I sat down to admire my handiwork, and congratulated myself on a good job well done. "You certainly can iron," I thought. "You are not fast, but thorough. OK, come on. Next. This isn't fishing or mending nets. Think of all the

37

inspirational messages you know: 'The difficult we will do right away; the impossible may take a little longer. The difficult we have done; the impossible we are doing. The impossible we have done; now we're working on the easy stuff.' Come on now; think. What other inspirational messages do we know?"

"Gentlemen in England now abed will hold their manhoods cheap——"

"WHO FOUGHT WITH US UPON SINN SWITHIN'S D――AAA――Y!"

"Good! (Not St. Swithin's Day, though. Whose *was* it? Never mind. Go on to something else; it'll come to you.)"

"Come on, you—ah—*guys!* Do you want to live forever?"

"And upon this charge,
CRY 'GOD FOR HADDY, ENGLAND, AND SINN GAWGE!'"

But not St. Swithin, though. Let's see; two syllables. Well, there's only one way to find out. I'll have to play the record. Can't look it up in the book; the print's too small.

I jumped up and dashed to the older girls' room where they were quietly crayoning amidst the rubble. "Shhhh!" I whispered. "Listen. How would you like to hear a real neat record? All right, but listen now, we can't play it loud and you have to be quiet, because Miranda's asleep." They were amenable—nay, eager. While getting out Sir Laurence Olivier's album of *Henry the Fifth* I convinced myself that this fifteen minutes would be time well spent.

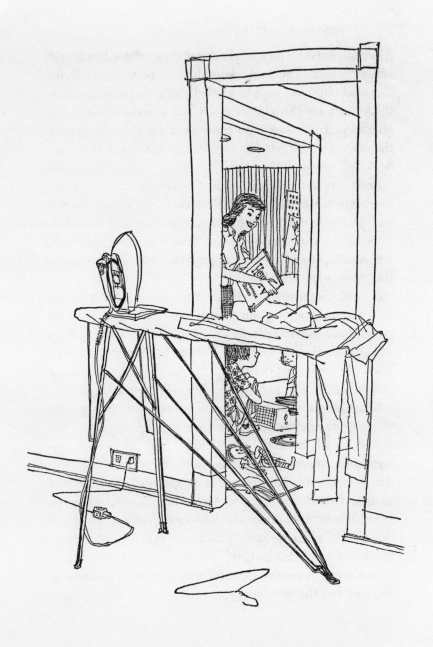

After all, even factory workers get time off for lunch and
coffee breaks. I'm not asking for an hour or anything
like that. Besides, isn't it a good thing to provide a cul-
tivated air for the children? Isn't it a good thing to be
able to make Shakespeare come alive for them as against
the way his marvel, his wonder, was hidden from me
by a dull teacher?

Soon we were caught up in the magic, and when the
records were finished, I was pleased to see that Louise
and Jennie had enjoyed it. Of course, they didn't understand it all, but they were not bored. By now, Miranda
was awake, so we decided to play the whole thing again,
this time nice and loud, so you could *really* hear the
sound of the arrows and the trumpets and everything.

We were hugging our knees; we were covered with
goose flesh—even Miranda was thrilled. We were soberly
sad at poor Harry's soliloquy: "Upon the King! Let us our
lives, our souls, our debts . . . lay on the King. We must
bear all. . . ." Oh, poor Harry, I know how it is.

One thing led to another, and soon I was sitting with
the big art encyclopedia open on my lap, saying: "The
movie is all in color, you know. And when you see
Katharine, there is this table, and it looks exactly like
this picture—see, kind of out of proportion—And she had
such a beautiful costume. And King Henry, when he
heard about the drummer boy being killed, he stood
there—and when he said 'I was not angry since I came
to France until this instant.'"

Just then, Jennie's attention was caught by something
she saw out the window.

"Louise, Miranda!" she yelled. "Come on!"

Before I could speak, they had opened the door and were running outside.

"Come back, come back," I called after them. "Where are you going?"

They halted their headlong flight, and as they came back to the house, Jennie was saying dejectedly: "Oh, he's gone and it was a chipmunk. Honestly! A real one. I sawl it. Honest!"

I slammed the door.

Louise and Miranda, disappointed at having missed the chipmunk, were prepared to doubt Jennie's avowals. "It was too a chipmunk! I *sawl* it!" Jennie shouted. "Just like the picture in my book—come on! I'll show you."

I trailed after them as they went to the tiny room where Jennie dived to the bottom of a pile of toys, books, dolls, and for all I knew, sandwiches, and came up immediately, waving the book in question. She opened it, and found a picture of a chipmunk which she triumphantly showed the other two.

"Listen," I asked, "do those things bite?"

I didn't wait for all the "Oh, Mother's" they can make so eloquent an expression of tried patience at parental thickheadedness. Withdrawing with dignity to the living room, I left them to continue with their nature study and to wonder what other marvels they might find here in the country. I looked at the clock—holy hat! There was no longer any time to wonder what I should do next. If I made each moment count, I might just be able to get two dinners, one for the children and one for

41

Hank and me, ready on time. "Don't panic," I said. "Whatever you do, don't panic." I whisked the ironed dress into a closet, put away the ironing board, and set the iron to cool on the table (*yes,* on an asbestos pad); I did all the dishes, dried them, put them away, made the beds, and helped the girls to clean up, all in less than twenty minutes. Then I looked at the children with a newly critical eye. Louise and Miranda didn't look too bad, but Jennie's costume was made up of so many colors that she looked like a bag of jelly beans. "At least your socks should match," I said irritably to Jennie. "Here; give me that red one and put on this blue one."

The curlers were soon out of my hair and it was brushed down on my shoulders (the way he likes it, though privately I thought the style a little dated). I skinned out of the outfit in which I had been insulting myself and the world at large all day, and then I looked nice in a skirt, blouse, and velvet flats.

Little hell now began—those hours between five and eight in the evening which must keep a lot of marriage counselors in pocket money. The children are at their most exhausted state—peevish, bored, far more restless than any prison inmate. So is the mother. Every day I prayed for the strength to get through these hours. I was still trying to preserve a little of the amenities by arranging for a separate dinner for Hank and me. This meant cooking and cleaning up after the children, seeing that they ate properly, keeping the house in one piece and the girls out of each other's hair. But, thank God, suddenly Daddy was home!

The children followed him while he washed up, and he listened, kindly and patiently, to everything—about the chipmunk, Mrs. Beige's visit, and the record: "It was wonderful, Daddy!" After washing, he picked up his baby and they sank into a comfortable chair while Louise and Jennie crowded close to them and told him how sweet he was, how good, how kind, how handsome. And he is, too.

Much as I hated to break up the tableau, I presently found it necessary to remind the girls that Daddy was hungry and tired, and that they had promised to play quietly while we had dinner. As soon as we were seated, and before I could even say, "Did you have a good day?" the interruptions began. The chops might just as well have been hockey pucks, so little were we aware of tasting them. As a matter of fact, they even looked like hockey pucks.

After dinner, Hank disappeared to help the girls get ready for bed, and I went back to the kitchen to attack the pots, pans, and dishes. Finally they were done and the children were in bed. With luck, they would giggle, walk around, get a glass of water, go to the bathroom, and sing, for only about an hour.

43

## 4

That night, as I lay in bed, sleepless and unhappy, my thoughts were on Alberta, our first and only maid. She was waiting for Louise and me when we came home from the hospital and she stayed with us all during our five years in New York. Now that we were living in Catatonia, and I was on my own, I missed her sorely and more fully appreciated all that she used to do so effortlessly. She had taught me to miter corners, not to wash stained things in hot water, to grease the bottom, but not the sides of, cake pans ("How would *you* like to climb a greased pole?"), and hundreds of other things I wished I could remember. She could do anything from making a dress to simonizing a car. What's more, she was *willing* to do anything.

Alberta had been born and brought up in Alabama, and despite her matter-of-fact efficiency, common sense, and fifteen years in the North, she had not been purged of her childhood belief in fairies and ghosts. Sometimes she would tell me of her experiences with the twilight world.

"One day I had to get up while it was still dark. I put on my new high heels and started out the apartment, and I no more than got to the first landing, when something say to me, plain as plain: 'You better go on back there and change them shoes.' So I did; I taken off my new shoes and I put on my old flats and went down and waited in the pitch dark for the bus."

"Well, what happened, Alberta?"

"Why nothing, Ma'am. But who knows what would have happened if I hadn't got the warning to go back there and change them shoes?"

Oh, Alberta, I thought, looking up into the dark, oh, how I miss you. Every time I spend the whole of three evenings sewing the waist back onto the skirt of a dress, only to have it come apart at the first wearing, oh, how I miss you.

Knowing that our budget would never allow itself to be stretched to include a maid's salary, I decided to stop longing for the impossible and concentrate instead on my worries. Like Mark Twain and others, I am convinced

45

that the things you worry about are the things that never happen, so instead of counting sheep (which even sheep fanciers must admit is pretty monotonous), I worry my way to sleep each night.

My chief worry right now was the speeders on our road. But what they could do was too frightening to think about for long, so I got that worry over with quickly. The bomb? Not tonight, please, not tonight. I was looking on vast empty, terribly empty space and the worst part of it was the silence—stop! Let's be more impersonal. Sheree North. Poor Sheree. They hired her just for that one part and gave her a big build-up till the movie was released and then dropped her. Whatever became of her? She has a daughter to support. I hope she has found work someplace. What will become of Harold Stassen? "Do Not Remove Under Penalty of the Law"—can they really do anything to me because I took that warning tag off the mattress? What the hell! It's *my* mattress. Why do all those families insist on living under that mountain, what's-it's-name, in Switzerland, I think, that is always about to destroy the whole village with an avalanche? I wish to heaven they would move someplace else, and that goes for those people under Vesuvius too.

That's enough, I then ordered myself. No more worries. I considered alternate ways of wooing sleep and finally thought, how about counting—ah, let's see—cities? Or, better still, songs. How about songs *about* cities? Why oh why oh why oh, did I ever leave Ohio—that's not a city. Let's see. April in Paris. A foggy day, in London Town. Petticoats of Portugal—where breezes play. Lady of Spain, I adore you! Valencia, inmyarmsIheldyour charmsbeneaththeblossomshighabove—whew! Wait till I catch my breath. All right now—go on. The rain in Spain. Granada, Granada, Granada, Gra—nah-—HAH—ha—hadada. In a little Spanish town, 'twas on a night like this. 'Twas not; no night was like this—ever. Spanish town. Don Juan. Don *John*—Don John of Austria is RIDING TO THE WARS. The wars? The Crusades. Crusades? Crusade—Billy Graham. Oh, no! Nonsense! Billy Graham has no plans for going to Spain. He's dedicated, yes, but not rash. Anyway, I comforted myself, they wouldn't do anything—probably just wouldn't let him get off the boat, is all.

I made up my mind to arise very early on the morning following and surprise Hank with real orange juice squeezed out of real oranges, oatmeal, and bacon and eggs. "You have some, too," I said, and was soon planning more than the basics; after a few minutes I could almost see, taste, and smell eggs benedict, fresh, homemade bread, golden waffles, and dainty sausages—I stopped myself just in time from stealing down to the kitchen. In fact, I caught myself with one leg out of bed. Drawing it back hastily, I said: "You don't need food now! You need *sleep*. Please, please, *go to sleep*." As I was obediently burrowing a way to a comfortable position in the bed, a sudden, fearful noise caused me to sit bolt upright.

I grabbed at Hank's shoulder and cried out, "Hank, wake up!" But the racket had awakened him and before I could pull myself together enough to get up, he had grabbed a flashlight and was running towards the room

47

where Louise and Jennie lay asleep. Oh, surely, I thought, as I finally managed to get up and make myself follow Hank on boneless legs, surely it can't be a burglar; no burglar would be so indiscreet. But how could I be sure? I was thinking of New York burglars; the masters, the virtuosi, the greats. Maybe this was the way they burgled in Catatonia.

When I arrived at Hank's side, he had opened the window and was beaming the flashlight downward, on a masked face!

"It *is* a burglar," I screamed. "Where's the phone? Call the police before he gets away!"

But all Hank did was flick the flashlight back and forth and start laughing.

"What's to laugh," I said, furiously. "What's so funny?" and I didn't find it at all hilarious when Hank explained that our burglar was only a raccoon raiding the garbage can. Long after Hank had finally gone back to sleep, I lay awake wondering if I would ever get used to country living. Finally I dozed, and then slept a sleep made hideous by dreams of a chipmunk chasing a raccoon chasing me. These dreams gave way to visions of Mrs. Beige, who was pacing the decks of a trireme and stopping to advise each slave, chained not to an oar but to a sink piled high with dishes, as follows: "Hard work never killed anybody."

The next evening we were planning to attend the town meeting. I had called the Rose Margaret Association of Gentlewomen and explained our need for a sitter and had been assured by a motherly, old-fashioned voice that my problems were over and that they would have one of their very best ladies at our house promptly at eight o'clock, and would I kindly send the check for the annual fee at once?

Since they were such ladies, I was anxious to make a good impression on them; I had scoured, scrubbed, and shined everything in the house, including the three girls. About twenty minutes before Mrs. Gemm was to arrive, Hank and I were dressed in our best and he was in the living room awaiting the lady, while I had the children gathered around me in the bedroom and was reading to them the story of Snow White. When we all heard a car drive up outside, I began to warn the girls once more to be very, very good.

Presently, the front door opened and a voice shouted: "Hello! Mr. Lamont? How's it going? Where's the kids? I just *love* kids. Don't you? I do. I just love kids. What's on the TV? Gonna have a little drink before you go—OK, but make mine a real shortie, hear? Don't wanta take no chances getting all slapped up, when we got the little ones to look after. No Sir, not old Molly. Should say not."

Hank sprinted into the bedroom, where we sat—he was enraged, but managed to speak calmly so the girls would not become more alarmed. "I'll have to take the lady home, Mama. Where does she live?"

I searched for her address while Hank soothed the children and we tried to ignore the singing in the other room. Finally I found the address and Hank went back to find that Mrs. Gemm had swiftly made the transition

from gaiety to unconsciousness. It took him some time
to try to rouse her with black coffee, give up, and carry
her bodily to her car, drive her home, and come back in
a taxi. During his absence I was firmly reassuring the
girls that we would not leave them alone and wishing
I could reassure myself that all sitters in Catatonia were
not like Mrs. Gemm. After the girls settled down and
went to sleep, I tried to be philosophical about the
predicament. I thought, well, it was an experience. But
at my age, who needs experience?

And I thought of Alberta. "I owe her a letter," I reminded myself. "Dear Alberta," I'll say. "Wish you were
here." But that wouldn't be true. Wish we were there—
that would be true.

## 5

Spring came to Catatonia, and I worked in the school
cafeteria, where I was naked to my enemies, without
chair, gun, or whip. I typed mile after mile of stencils.
I ran off league after league of mimeographs. I faith-
fully attended each PTA meeting, and religiously
remained to clean up the ash trays and coffee cups.

Disappointed at finding myself in the ranks of un-
skilled labor, along with a few other mothers whom
Mrs. Beige had had on the hip, I did all that was expected
of me, hoping that my abilities would be recognized by

Those Who Ran Things. I reasoned that if fairness prevailed, I would be rewarded with a board membership in the PTA at the very least. Eventually, however, it began to sink home that the only people aware of my zeal were children, bus drivers, cafeteria workers, and a few other mothers who were patsies like me. Worthy as these fellow creatures were, they were not Those Who Ran Things.

In all this, Hank was no help. He did go to a couple of meetings, but the atmosphere left him cold. He didn't like to see the principal and teachers standing with uncertain feet on the rubble which displaced the pedestals these people had occupied in his youth. The last discussion we had about his poor record in the matter of "taking an active interest" ended abruptly when he said, "There is no PTA at Harvard, and at Harvard, *nobody* calls a professor 'George.'"

Besides the PTA, there were numerous other organizations. In Catatonia, where there were more real estate agents than houses, it was not surprising that there were more civic organizations than people. I attended a few meetings of these leagues, associations, and clubs, but only a few. For all the sense I could make out of most of the discussions, they might as well have been conducted in Old Church Slavonic. What little I did understand seemed to indicate that commuter families were regarded more as intruders than citizens, that new families joined organizations for much the same reason that pioneers traveled in wagon trains.

One of the organizations put up posters bearing the query: "How are you going to feel about YOUR TOWN twenty years from now?" If I happened to feel optimistic, my reply was, "Apathetic, at best." I hoped that the passage of time would find me climbing slowly from terror, to animosity, to apathy. That was as far as I allowed myself to go. In my really black moments, the sight of one of the posters had a more pronounced effect— the idea that I might be living in Catatonia for twenty years tempted me to suicide.

To me, the worst feature of the place was the total, absolute, complete lack of privacy. Used to the anonymity of the metropolis, I found it unnerving to be constantly intruded upon. I discovered all too soon that Mrs. Beige was but the motorcycle police in advance of a parade of the uninvited.

One afternoon, after so many people had come to my house unasked that I stopped counting, I wasn't even surprised when a little boy I had never seen before opened the front door. He was not more than two years old. Seeing me, he shouted a gay greeting.

"Murp!"

"It all depends," I replied. "Is that a capital 'M' or a small 'm'?"

The child grinned cheerfully, and it pleased me to see that I was getting through to him. He removed his coat, hat, and boots, and laid the garments neatly on the living-room floor, each in a different place. A fastidious young man, I thought. Since he could have dropped his clothes all in a heap, or allowed them to trail after him one by one, I was taken by his considerateness. Then he spoke again.

53

"Murp!"

"All right," I answered, "if you don't care what you say."

Miranda came into the room, attracted by the voices. I was glad to see her. "Hello!" she cried, hugging the little boy happily. "Let's go outside and I'll show you a giant ant I stepped on."

"Who's your friend, Miranda?" I asked.

"I don't know," she answered. "He's brand new."

She regarded the boy approvingly—more approvingly than I. "Listen, Miranda," I said. "Please ask him what his name is, and where he lives."

Miranda nodded solemnly, as if to put me at my ease, and turned to the boy. "What's your name?" she asked him. "Where do you live?"

The child's face brightened. He said something to Miranda that sounded like "Chevans," and then something that sounded like he was trying to speak one of the more obscure Welsh dialects. "Domowmuvvermame owlwherrilich." Though not an accurate rendering, it's the best I can do.

Miranda relayed the message. "He says his first name is Charles Evans, but he doesn't know his last name, or where he lives." Then, her duties as translator over, she turned to Charles Evans. "Come on. I'll show you the ant, and then we'll play house. I'll be the father, and you be the mother, because I'm the biggest."

"Bigger," I said mechanically.

"Murp!" Charles Evans said.

Just before they left to inspect the ant remains, Charles

Evans reverted to Welsh. "He says his mother has gone shopping and will be back for him in an hour," Miranda reported.

After they departed I toyed with the idea of looking in the phone book under the H's. "But no," I thought. "Even if Miranda is right, and he *is* called Charles Evans, it simply can't be." Besides, Mrs. Hughes wasn't home; Mrs. Hughes had gone shopping—always assuming that Miranda's translation had been correct.

Several hours later, during which time the two older girls had come home from school and were playing with Miranda and Charles Evans in the living room, a piquant auto horn sounded outside. "Mommy!" Charles Evans shouted. As soon as I got him into his outdoor clothes, he bolted. I hurried after him, just in time to see him drive off with his mother, but not in time for me to have a word with her. "Isn't it wonderful," I mused, "how a little child can tell the sound of his own mother's Dauphine horn from all the rest?" Returning to the chores of the hour, I decided, "It must be a capital "M" in Murp."

With the experience of Charles Evans behind me, I felt I owed it to myself to keep the doors locked at least. I was even inclined to take the drastic step of having the phone removed.

If it was not goodwife Francesca calling about some meeting, it was a salesman who was saving shoe leather and gasoline. Oh, how often I wished that Thomas A. Watson had laid a restraining hand on A. G. Bell's arm and had said to him, "Let's not and say we did." Some of the salesmen I could have strangled, but I loved them

each and every one as compared to the lady who called, cheery as a lark, and said, "Congratulations! You have been chosen as a typical American family, to receive our gift of a free cemetery lot as soon as you purchase four others." I am not a plan-ahead type. I know that we all have to go sometime, but I believe that spur-of-the-moment get-togethers are always the most successful.

It was over the telephone that I agreed, in what I now look back upon as the weakest of all my weak moments, to supervise the turtle races at a certain fair. The turtles were bad enough—my feeling sorry for them and hating to touch them producing an emotional crisis—but the peak of the day was yet to come. Grazie, wearing an official's badge, approached and took me by the arm. "Bumpy will take over the turtles. Come with me."

She led me to a small, roped-off square, in the middle of which was a wooden stool. She directed me to sit on the stool. Since she seemed much too busy to answer questions, and since I was too confused to think of any questions to ask, I sat. Grazie then handed me a large plastic space helmet, and helped me to put it on. (What do you do when you are handed a large plastic space helmet, except put it on?) "This is one of our most popular attractions. The small boy who was supposed to be the target went and got the mumps. Here's what you do—just sit here in your helmet. When you get a customer, give him these arrows—" (I was handed a fistful of arrows) "—and put this cork on top of your helmet. The cork works by suction. Like this. See? If the customer shoots the cork off—he gets three arrows for a quarter—the bow is over there—if he shoots it off, he gets one of the Kewpies. But be careful to find the cork. It's the only one we have."

With this admonition she was off, leaving me to face a mob of youngsters, each one panting to have first crack at me. The blunt, rubber-tipped arrows were harmless enough, in theory and I suppose in fact, but even so I flinched. And I am proud to say that after my second customer managed to displace the cork, I immediately decided that I couldn't find it, and quietly removed my helmet and went home. If the small boy whose unwilling substitute I was could get the mumps, so could I.

Walking home in the sunset, and asking myself a single question—"This is life far from the madding throng?"—I deeply regretted the scarcity of those who were described in the immortal words of Francesca as "dreary little housewives." "If only there were more of them," I wished, "less Murp, and more of them so I could be at one with them. They also serve who but stay home and mind their business."

## 6

By the end of spring, I had been conditioned to view life
in the suburbs with a perpetual "what next" attitude. I
was nonetheless shocked, however, to realize that we had
become involved with the underworld. This association
was inescapable. As homeowners, we were required to
invest in various household appliances; it followed that
we had to deal with certain local shopkeepers and servicemen—Robin Hoods in reverse, who steal from the poor
and give to the rich (themselves).

Buying and caring for household appliances was a

field in which we had had no experience. In Manhattan, when washday came around, either Alberta or I would put a quarter, and the clothes, into one of many washer-dryers in the basement of the apartment house. After a reasonable time, there were the clothes, clean and dry. The stove, refrigerator, and air-conditioning unit in the apartment all belonged to the management, and, curious though it may seem, I can't remember anything going wrong with any of them. Besides, if anything ever did, it wasn't our problem.

Washing clothes in Catatonia was a more complicated affair—it meant taking them to the laundry, or buying your own washing machine. I knew full well that I was not of M.I.T. caliber, but reasoning that if other women could learn to operate a washing machine, so could I, I bought one. The salesman was firm, even vehement, in his assurance that the Wonderful Old Machine (that's the brand name of the thing; it was manufactured by the Wonderful Old Washing Machine Company of Norton, Ohio) was the latest, best, and most beautiful appliance created by modern engineers. So was the guarantee that accompanied the machine. Both it and the salesman promised a year's free service, a full demonstration of the marvels this machine was capable of, and replacement and/or prompt repair of all parts that might fail to function.

The serviceman who finally arrived to install the machine (it was two weeks before "finally") proved to be the biggest bungler since Ethan Frome. He inspected the expensive, extensive new wiring and fuse box we had

had installed just to accommodate the washer, and pronounced them "OK." He then shoved corrugated paper
under the retractable legs of the machine, instead of
adjusting them to compensate for the unevenness of the
floor. ("A fig for you," one felt he thought, "you smart-

aleck engineers.") After telling me we should have bought the newest Ecstasy Washing Machine, instead of the Wonderful Old, he left. That was the demonstration.

Thereafter, whenever I tried to use the machine, it would leap insanely as it went into high spin. The door would burst open and the water, clothes, and detergent would fume from the machine and onto the floor. After several calls to the salesman, which were answered by an aloof, detached voice which said the salesman was: (1) out of town, (2) deep in conference, (3) in the bathroom, I tried to get in touch with the serviceman. He returned my fifth or sixth call to his answering service, and although he was undisguisedly bored, he agreed to "stop by in a couple days." When I tried to impress him with the urgency of my need, he said he didn't consider washing machines an emergency. "Refrigerators, they're an emergency," he philosophized. "Washers, they ain't."

In time, he came to call. He inspected the machine, and decided that the reason the appliance was misbehaving was that the fuse box was the wrong kind. "You gotta have a circuit breaker," was his diagnosis. (He airily dismissed my reminder that he had seemed to like the fuse box on his first tour of inspection.)

Not quite in desperation, but next door to it, I appealed directly to the Wonderful Old Washing Machine Company. I threatened that if they didn't repair the machine satisfactorily, I would take my case straight through to the Supreme Court. Within ten days, the manufacturer's representative came to see me, but refused to lift a finger to help when he learned the source of my supply. I was

informed, coldly, that my salesman had been disenfran-
chised. This means that he was a sort of unfrocked
dealer; he had been refused permission to sell Wonderful
Olds because of price-cutting, or some such National
Association of Manufacturers' mortal sin. The representative pointed out that I was in possession of a washing
machine whose serial number had been filed off, a piece
of intelligence that left me stiff with fright. Could it be, I
wondered, that we had a hot machine? When weeks went
by and nobody came to arrest me as the receiver of stolen
property, I became less apprehensive and tried to find a
capable repairman. I found such a man, at length, and
he charged $150 to fix the damage done by the original
serviceman. Time passed, and the washer performed
reasonably well, but I still felt that there was much to be
said in defense of the good old days when housekeepers
dealt with soiled clothing by taking it to the nearest brook
and pounding it with rocks—hard on the clothes, but
certainly less of a strain on the nervous system.

I resolved that I would resist any temptation to add
more appliances to the house, with the exception of a
dishwasher—if we could ever afford it. "But I will be
absolutely, positively sure of the honesty of the seller
before I buy," I promised myself.

There was nothing else in the way of appliances we
needed. We had a refrigerator and a stove that had been
left by the former owners of the house. The refrigerator,
being very old, performed admirably. It made ice quickly,
and kept food fresh. And it had other qualities I
appreciated; it was self-effacing, quiet, and dependable.

The stove wasn't as satisfactory. It was much too big for the little kitchen and, of its four burners, only one worked. But I can't say that I ever felt any hostility to the stove, nor a strong desire for a new one. The fact that we found ourselves the owners of a new refrigerator-freezer and a new stove, within six months after bedding down in Catatonia, wasn't my fault. It was the supermarket's fault.

One Saturday I entered the store, having left Hank and the children to wait for me in the car. As usual, I braced myself for the customary struggle involved in extracting a cart from the apparently mile-long row. I knew that the one I would succeed in dislodging would either have one or two wheels canted, or one or more wheels missing. In the latter case, the cart would be unpushable. I hoped for the canted-wheel model, even though its use made my progress through the store appear influenced by drink. Better that than having to carry one of the wheel-missing unpushables in my arms.

After a protracted tug-of-war, a cart allowed itself to be separated from its fellows, and I paused to regain my breath before entering the center of the arena. I looked up at the large portraits of affable, hygienic, wholesome men and women that adorn our supermarket, and which are supposed to represent the clerks. The difference between the prototypes and the portraits fascinated me. The former, every man jack and woman, seemed to be misanthropes who hated even the concept of customers. And the legend under the portraits, "All that we are, or ever hope to be, we owe to you, our valued customers," struck me as the freest kind of free verse—more than free, untrammelled.

Sighing, I joined the crowd of shoppers and reached into a pocket for my shopping list. It wasn't there. In my mind's eye, I could see it, careful and concise, hanging on the bulletin board in our kitchen, where I had left it. I remembered that the list was to remind me, among other things, about peanut butter and Penny Pitou. Peanut butter I could understand (we always needed peanut butter), but what was the Penny Pitou? A cereal premium? That must be it, I decided. I must buy a box of cereal that has a Penny Pitou in it. But what else? The crowd was moving me along as I was trying to remember, and suddenly I thought "eggs." But it was too late. I was past the egg department, and it wasn't considered cricket to buck the crowd. The only people who did so were children who had been left by their mothers to roam at will in the store. They enjoyed themselves hugely; they raced up and down the aisles yelling as if they were on fire; and they knocked down large glass containers of catsup, ammonia, bleach, and syrup.

I arrived at the meat counter and discovered that the ladybutcher had come out from behind the counter. Bellowing to the manager information regarding coffee breaks, she walked backward in my direction. Rapidly. Too late, I tried to get myself and my cart out of her way. We collided. She glared at me, and, since she was carrying a bloody cleaver, I said, "Oh, please forgive me!"

By now I was halfway through the store and my cart was still empty. This realization brought me to despair and as I was being pushed along, I reached out and grabbed a shelf. Since I had bottlenecked the crowd, I felt I had to select something, so I chose a ten-pound sack of sugar even though I had at least eight pounds at home. The sugar in my possession, we all surged forward once more. I had almost reached the end of that particular aisle when a woman, in tones of unmatchable stridency, reproached me for leaking sugar. I looked back and saw that she was right. I had indeed been trailing sugar. There was a momentary lull in the uproar—the crowd stared silently while I made my way back to return the damaged bag. I tried to pick out another, but changed my mind when I noticed that each package of sugar had had a small, neat hole punched in its side.

Sugarless, I hastened on and soon arrived at the check-out stations. Since my cart was still empty, I went back to the entrance and began my pilgrimage anew. I got my hands on two jars of peanut butter as I was being swept along, and continued till I reached the cereal display. Here, it was like the eye of a hurricane—peaceful—so I stopped to relax and inspect the latest tricks that had been played on oats, wheat, rice, and barley.

When I arrived at the check-out counter for the second time, I had in my basket twelve different kinds of cereal (none of which said on the box that there was a "Penny Pitou" inside) and two jars of peanut butter. I tried to decide between going around again, thus delaying the most dreadful feature of the shopping trip—the check-out counter—or facing it at once and escaping to the relative quiet of our car.

66

Taking a deep breath, I elected to get it over with. I approached the check-out counter and saw that the "speed-up" aisle (for those shoppers buying less than fifteen items) was choked as usual by people with one or more carts piled high with merchandise. I stood at the end of the shortest line of shoppers, where a large woman soon approached me, smiled winningly, and said: "Excuse me."

"Certainly," said I, and moved back so that she could get by. The lady said, "Thank you," and took my place in the line.

Standing there waiting, I tried to prepare for the inevitable advent of the woman destined to get in line behind me. She arrived all too soon, as I could tell by the slight, but inexorable, pressure against the small of my back. ("Here we go again," I thought.) I knew it was useless, but I inched forward, as far as possible. The lady behind me—who never pushes—nothing so obvious—followed with the same quiet persistence. I have a permanent bruise across my back as a result of being subjected, every week, to this gentle, unyielding, nagging nudge.

I have invented a small order-customer separator which I am thinking of having patented, and which supermarkets should be glad to install. It is a little, but effective, guillotine which automatically will chop off the hands of anyone who puts as much as a box of toothpicks on the check-out counter before the departure of the preceding customer. Also, I am working on an electrical attachment for the front of supermarket carts. This device is designed to send about fifty to one hundred volts from the cart handle into the nudger, as soon as the front of her cart makes contact with the back of the customer in front of her. (The latter invention is more difficult to perfect; I haven't yet figured out a way of protecting the nudgee from the electricity.)

The lady cashier finished bagging the order of the customer ahead of me, said, "Right back," and disappeared. I waited for some time, all the while being leaned on slightly by the woman behind me. During the cashier's absence, I occupied myself with keeping my temper and separating my order from hers. At last the cashier returned, but my hopes of getting outside in less than half an hour declined and died as I saw that the manager was hot on her heels. The manager summarily waved the cashier aside, and began to check the cash register. The cashier briskly snapped her gum, the woman behind shoved faintly, and we all waited silently, with mutual loathing, while the manager counted the money. He eventually decided that all was well with his till, and it wasn't long after that—not really—that I was allowed to pay for my purchases and depart.

When I got inside the car, I asked Hank: "Does 'Penny Pitou' mean anything to you?"

"Well," he temporized, "I have nothing against her—don't tell me *she's* in there!"

"Who's in where?" I asked, and turned to stop the children from running into the supermarket. I headed them off and forced them back into the car, while they kept protesting that they wanted to go inside and see Penny Pitou. "*Who* is Penny Pitou?" I demanded.

"She's the United States Olympic skiing contender,"

answered Hank. Then I remembered why I had written down the name. I had heard the girls discussing her, and had made a note to ask Hank who she was.

That question settled, we all went home, but when Hank saw what was in the shopping bags, he went right out again. By then he was hungry, not having had lunch, so his purchases strained the food budget beyond endurance.

Any fair-minded person would agree that the blame for my falling for the frozen-food salesman must be attributed to the supermarket. The salesman came to call on the following Monday, while I was still trying to recover from the shopping expedition. His message was that we would be given a combination freezer-refrigerator free, because once in possession of this appliance, we would be entitled to buy our food at wholesale prices, and this great saving would pay for the freezer. But what interested me most about his story was his assurance that never again—positively never—would we have to visit the supermarket. He stated that his company—Mother Shipton's Food Club—would begin sending us everything necessary to the sustenance of life, as soon as I ordered the appliance. Not only that, he also promised that we, as dear friends of Mother Shipton's, would be permitted to buy soap, paper, cigarettes, even wines, beer, and liquors, also at wholesale prices. It was the most intriguing proposition I had ever heard in my life. When the salesman left, he carried with him a long legal document bearing my clear signature.

Naturally, I didn't go into this deal blindly, without making sure of the salesman's claims. He mentioned the names of several prominent Catatonics who were blissful members of the club and this, along with his tales about the superior qualities of his food, sold me. When Hank came home that night, I could hardly wait to tell him the good news. He wasn't nearly so enthusiastic as I had expected. In fact, when he saw my copy of the agreement with the food people, he turned white. I couldn't quite make out what he said afterwards: something to the effect that I had spent $1,000, less $100 which the salesman allowed on our old, perfectly good, refrigerator.

It pains me to tell you that Hank's turning pale was justified. After a week or two, my complexion assumed the same hue more and more frequently, as it became increasingly evident that the frozen-food venture was a total failure. The freezer-refrigerator was dumped in the middle of the kitchen one morning, from a truck which drove right up to the door, heedless of the damage it caused the flagstone path and the steps leading to the door.

Three men dragged the appliance into the kitchen, threw one (1) dented ice-cube tray onto the table, and left without a word. We waited for several days for a serviceman to install the machine; finally, Hank enlisted the help of a neighbor and moved it into a corner.

Although I called the company over and over, my attempts to get service on the machine, which was loud, temperamental, and unruly, were unsuccessful. Checking with other customers of Mother Shipton's, I learned that I was one more dissatisfied among their number. When I learned that the most expensive butcher shop in town, a virtual Tiffany among butcher shops, sold beef for two cents a pound less than the frozen-food people, my humiliation was complete. And we still went shopping at the supermarket every week.

I forgot to mention one thing—since there was not enough room in the kitchen for both the stove and the new freezer-refrigerator, we were forced to get a new stove. I visited a local store which had been in business since 1915. The owner commiserated with me on my past experiences with the washing-machine people and the frozen-food people. He then sold me a twenty-inch stove, the only size that would now fit in the kitchen. Being so small, the stove was considered "special"; it cost fifty dollars more than the most de luxe model of regulation size.

The stove man couldn't give me any cash allowance on our old stove, for which he apologized, but he graciously agreed to dispose of it. I suspected that the fortune he made when he sold me my new stove, and someone else my old one, enabled him to retire. He closed down shortly thereafter.

I didn't know that he had gone out of business until, about a month after we purchased the stove, I called to say that it wouldn't work. My call was answered by a Janissary who, in a gruff voice, said, " 'Sonly nine-thirty. Call back after ten," and hung up. Miffed, I hung up, too. When I called back after ten, a secretary told me that the store was no longer in business; she was just there to close the books. She listened to my story, but wouldn't believe it.

"That was our very best model," she declared.

"No wonder you went out of business," I said.

After a few more brief exchanges of cordiality, she promised to have the owner call, "when he comes in."

Well, I guess he didn't "come in" till about five-thirty that afternoon—it wasn't until then that he called. In the meantime, I grew fearful of the possible necessity of cooking in the living-room fireplace and, calling the hardware store, I ordered an automatic coffeemaker. I simply couldn't bear the prospect of waiting for the fireplace to boil water before I could have my morning coffee. When the former appliance-store owner at last called back, and heard of the stove's defection, he said, "Just go downstairs and put in a new fuse."

"WHO, ME?"

"All right, then," he said, "I'll come over and do it, but it'll cost you!"

He came over, and it did cost me—$7.50. But anyway, after that the stove cooked for about four or five months. Then one evening Hank arrived home to find me wearing his rubber hip boots and my own rubber gloves while I cooked dinner. I explained that I had been severely shocked by the stove, and that although I had called several electricians, none had seemed anxious for employment. One said fixing my stove would put him into a higher income-tax bracket; he scoffed at my suggestion that he could square himself with the Department of Internal Revenue if he would but lower his service charge. Another expert *said* he would come, but didn't.

Two days later, I managed to coax an electrician over to the house. Firmly denying that the stove could give me a shock (because, he said, "all electric stoves are grounded"), he expressed the belief that—always assuming I had been shocked at all—something else must have been guilty. He produced a little wire thing from his bag of tricks, and with it he tried the iron, the toaster, the waffle grill, and the coffeemaker, and pronounced them inoffensive. Since he wouldn't believe me about the stove, he then packed up his gear and was about to leave. By appealing to his sporting instincts, I persuaded him to test the stove (I bet him a dollar). When he did, he got a veritable doozey of a shock and I hurriedly left the kitchen. After a brief interval, he called out an "all-clear," and I returned.

"What was wrong?" I asked.

"Fella that installed the stove, he forgot to ground it," he replied.

"Do you mean to tell me that I have been cooking, for six months, on an ungrounded, 220-volt stove?" I cried. "I might have been killed!"

"Nah," said the electrician. "Very seldom anybody gets electrocuted by house current."

"I heard of a case!" I insisted. "I read about a man who was electrocuted at home, by just little old house current!"

"Yeah," he answered, "but the conditions have to be ideal."

Then, welching on the dollar bet, he left.

When I ponder on appliance servicemen and salespeople, I am reminded of my mother. I think of how she used to look at me whenever I arrived home, triumphantly bearing a "bargain," and how she would say, "They saw you coming." When I protested that my new hat, or dress, or shoes, had been marked down from $35 to $2.95, my mother would only add, "And you believed them."

## 7

Let us skip lightly over our first summer in Catatonia. Let us just note the high spots. I met moles and possums and mice. I saw deer leaping majestically across the road. I surprised skunks moving about in the twilight, carrying themselves with a dignity that Queen Mary might have envied. If I did not get used to the nightly raids of the raccoons (how could you get *used* to it?), I learned how not to be surprised by them. And after I almost picked up the first snake I saw, thinking, as have many others before me, that it was a stick, I began to lift up my knees to my chest whenever I walked outside, and thus developed a habit that stayed with me indoors as well, which caused Louise to ask me if I was practicing to be a drum majorette.

To my store of information and experience, I also added bugs. Mice I dislike, rats I hate, but bugs I truly loathe. The first spider who moved in on us was at least two inches wide. He looked like a Rorschach Test. What I did about him was to cover him with a box, and then shut him and the box up in the room where he had appeared, declaring that room out of bounds. This was inconvenient, as I should have realized beforehand, because the room with the spider was the room with the bath and other plumbing, and it would be hours before Hank got home.

"That's just a tree spider," he said, after arriving home and disposing of the beast.

I can't say for sure, because I haven't been able to prove it, but I still think to this day that Hank made up the name "tree spider," hoping to prove that he had been around such things all his life (as he hadn't) and knew from intimate experience that they were harmless. And when the ants arrived (oh yes, millions of them) and began carrying out their gravely important projects all over the house, he dismissed them casually as "carpenter ants." Having these creatures identified, and given pet names, did not endear them to me.

What added most to my feeling of unreality, of having wandered into an animated cartoon, was that all these unhuman beings were much more at home around our place than I was. June wasn't half over when I decided

john huehnergarth

that Mr. Gershwin should have written that line: "Summertime! And the livin' is *easy?*"

Looking back, I can find only three good things to say about that summer. The first good thing was that it was always cool at night. The second good thing was that I had, so far, survived. The third good thing was the birds. They came in numbers—birds I never knew; birds I could never have imagined—blue, red, orange, brown, and shiny blue-black. These last, I knew. They were crows, and they rapidly became my dearest, most amusing friends. To learn that they had a bad reputation surprised me. I developed a strong ill-will for a man who lived nearby and who was always shooting at them, simply because he had planted some corn which he said they robbed. But how did he know which crows were the robbers? Even if corn-stealing were a capital offense, which it isn't, he was certainly carrying the guilt-by-association theory to excess, and killing a lot of innocent birds. But then I have never been able to understand why anyone should want to shoot anything. I would just as soon skip the next safari. Guns have always been anathema to me, and that's another reason why I so often longed to be back in New York—in New York you could be fairly sure that the neighbors wouldn't be shooting off guns.

And also in New York, you could be fairly sure that few, if any, men would be walking around in Bermuda shorts! Now that it was summer and the ladies had changed into their summer uniform, shucked the woolen socks and exchanged the woolen Bermudas for chino Bermudas, the woolen shirts for cotton, and covered their crew cuts with baseball caps—added to this scene of *haute couture* was the sight of men of all sizes and shapes dressed in Bermuda shorts and shirts. The shirts were worn outside the shorts and were unbuttoned way down to the navel, and often past it. It looked as if they were all trying to prove they had had mothers. Every time I went in town, I felt as if I would never be able to make it through that jungle of hairy chests and legs. I could not help thinking how nice even the least Adonis-like of them would look in a nice pair of white ducks or flannels and in a regular shirt, with only the top one or two buttons opened. I passed one of these men one day, as he was declaiming to a fellow glass of fashion: "I'm a lifelong Republican!"

"Then why don't you button your shirt?" I hissed when I was well out of his hearing.

Another thing that lingers in my memory as part of that summer is the sight and the sound of lots of water. There was a beach in Catatonia—not much of a beach, but a beach—and somehow the notion arose that I was supposed to enjoy it. Swimming was proposed, and picnics on the sand. All that interfered, once again, were my own limitations. I don't like swimming and I don't like picnics on the sand, or anywhere else for that matter. But in a spirit of comradeship and because I didn't want the girls to think I was afraid of the water, *too,* I allowed myself to be persuaded to go along. Just twice, however. The first time I came home looking like the inspiration for shocking pink, and the second time, when I swathed myself head to foot like one of the Museum of Natural History's better-dressed mummies, tragedy struck before

I even got home. Miranda begged me to wade with her in the incoming tide, which I did, and then I fell in. It wasn't getting wet that I minded; it was the struggle to get out, bound as I was, and looking like a patch of floating seaweed. So I shelved my spirit of comradeship, and let Hank and the girls go to the beach without me. I stayed home and did the crossword puzzles in the Sunday *Times*. On red-letter days, I even did the double what-do-you-call-it. It was at these times that I really felt sorry for Hank and the girls, running in and out of the water down there, and never accomplishing anything.

It was also during this summer that Hank proposed we get a dog. I went along with the idea, hoping that a dog would keep some of the forest beasts at bay, and I must say that we all fell in love with D'Arcy on sight. He was a Dalmatian, of noble bearing and intelligent appearance. I thought he was aptly named. I could imagine one of his distinguished ancestors running beside the coach of someone like the Scarlet Pimpernel, and being a splendid assistant in various deeds of swashbuckling heroism. I admired D'Arcy extravagantly. We were assured by the kennel from which he was purchased that he was housebroken, fond of children, and totally commendable in every respect. And never mind, I told myself, that he is so tall.

How soon disillusionment set in I don't remember; I think it was less than twenty-four hours after we brought D'Arcy home. Noble in bearing he was. Intelligent-looking he was. And also he was a fraud. What D'Arcy was, basically, was a comedian. Or, to give him as much credit as possible, it could be that something happened to his psyche when he joined us. With fine disregard for the thought that had gone into his christening, the girls called him "Dorothy," and "Dorothy" he remained. His initial example of fecklessness was falling down the stairs. That happened the first evening he shared our abode. The next thing we observed was that he fancied himself as a small, cuddly dog. Waiting till one of his loved ones was seated, Dorothy-D'Arcy would fling himself, in an abandonment of emotion, up and onto the lap of the loved one, thereby practically knocking the loved one unconscious.

One incident stands out in my mind as being typical, not only of Dorothy-D'Arcy, but of what I remember as the panorama of idiocy that made up my nights and days. Early one afternoon this noble beast knocked over a lamp, and ate some glass from the resultant broken light bulb. I rushed to the yellow pages of the phone book, called the first vet I could find listed there, and was advised by him to hurry the dog to his office right away. Since I didn't know how to drive, and since I could imagine all sorts of ghastly things happening to the insides of Dorothy-D'Arcy, I hired a taxi for the daffy dog. It turned out that the vet was a three-dollar ($3) ride away, without tip, which had to be considerable, as I had to persuade the driver to deliver the patient without my being with him. They made quite a sight as the girls and I watched them drive off—Dorothy-D'Arcy sitting straight and proud on the back seat, almost saying, as he looked from the window: "Sure I'm riding in a taxi. Doesn't everybody?"

Purged, pronounced sound, and home again, this best friend of man next sought diversion by tangling with a skunk. Again I called the vet, who said, "Oh, how unfortunate," and that if he wasn't all full up, every nook and cranny, he would be glad to take in my pet (*pet!*) and give him a nice antiseptic bath. "But what should I *do?*" I asked. "Use tomato juice," he advised. Restraining the sarcastic impulse that prompted me to ask if I was supposed to pour the tomato juice on the dog, I inquired politely, instead:

"But Doctor, what if I can't make him drink it?"

"Don't try to make him drink it," the impatient voice replied. "Pour the tomato juice on the dog."

See? It is axiomatic. You ask a silly question, you get a silly answer.

It has been long held, I believe, that one can learn to live with any situation. But by the time I had learned to live with Dorothy-D'Arcy and he had learned to live with me, each in our own wild way, the poor thing was killed. And by a speeder, of course. He left our place one day, apparently taken by some spirit of high adventure, and though the girls and I called and called, he didn't come back. I reported his absence to the dog warden, and we waited for Dorothy-D'Arcy to return. He didn't. Just as we were about to sit down to dinner, the dog warden returned my call. Fortunately Hank was there to answer the phone. We didn't eat any dinner. Nobody was hungry. I had a new worry that night, dark and fierce, and what I worried about was whether D'Arcy (I couldn't call him Dorothy any more) would forgive all my rude remarks to and about him, wherever he was. Summer ended with D'Arcy. A few days later, as I stood outside, missing him, I saw that the first leaves were beginning to turn.

## 8

On a crisp morning early in September, at one of those times when I found myself sitting on the kitchen floor, Hank gone and the girls not yet upon me, I was dodging complete wakefulness by musing upon the latest plans that persons other than ourselves had for disposing of Hank's salary. We recently had received, among other glad tidings, the news that our oil burner again needed extensive repairs: three hundred dollars' worth. I sat there on the floor, trying at the command of my better self to forgive the joyous way in which the repairman had mentioned three hundred dollars. That was hard. What was impossible was to forgive him his brand-new Porsche —not so much the idea of his owning the vehicle, but the fact that we were buying it for him. I was convinced that our money, less the one or two dollars the repairman would spend on a couple of oil-burner screws and bolts, would take care of the next installment.

Feeling an urge to express my resentment, I gazed at the wall nearest me and addressed the house:

"Some of us have a little pride," I said. "But *you*— whatever *you* want, you can have. A new roof? Coming right up. A new field for your precious septic tank? Please, be my guest. You can't stand those termites another minute? Very well; the termites must go.

"Spoiled," I concluded, "spoiled rotten."

This diatribe relieved my feelings, but not enough, so I kicked the wall nearest to me. The kick dislodged a small pamphlet that was resting on the top of the radiator and, fascinated, I watched the little book float down lazily, like an autumn leaf. As it came to rest on the floor I reached out idly and picked it up. Anything to read is better than nothing to read, and a glance at the pamphlet's title assured me that a few minutes' attention to it would not be time wasted. Surely I might be forgiven for letting the children rest a while longer while I improved my mind.

"Popular Superstitions." I felt a bit the way I imagined William Shakespeare might have felt had he come upon a pamphlet called "Helpful Hints on Writing Blank Verse."

On the subject of superstitions, I considered myself an authority.

It should be apparent by now that I am an awful, arrant, coward. Others may lead the foolhardy life if it pleases them, but not me. I try to keep out of the way of disaster. I keep shoes off tabletops, and hats off beds. I avoid walking under ladders, stepping on cracks in the pavement, and starting journeys on Fridays. I carry any number of charms, amulets, and similar items, and I have secretly sewn lucky pieces into the linings of Hank's and the children's clothes. Secretly, because I do not relish being sneered at by unbelievers.

Though I felt sure I knew just about everything there was to know about good, and bad, luck, I was willing to let this pamphlet inform me further, if it could. Certainly our luck since moving to Catatonia had been nothing to merit a cheer. It was possible that I had missed out on something.

See a pin and pick it up, all the day you'll have good luck.

If you pass a load of hay, your wish will come true that very day.

Leave a hat upon the bed, be not surprised when love has fled.

When I came upon that old chestnut about throwing salt over your left shoulder after you have accidentally spilled some, I was ready to concede that I was wasting my time. The very floor on which I sat was proof that I didn't have to be informed about *that* rite; after a couple of salt spillings while I was getting dinner the night before, it was as grainy as sandpaper. I thought fleetingly about arousing the girls, and then, turning my mind back to the pamphlet, I flipped a couple of pages and read:

It is bad luck to bring an old broom into a new house.

For an instant I was too dazzled to think—at long last, after these months in Catatonia, everything was becoming clear. "But *now* they tell me," I said to myself. "What good does it do me *now?*" Immediately, my thoughts winged back to Alberta. No wonder she had left that broom out at the incinerator on moving day. I had thought Alberta, the impeccable, had made a mistake! And *I* had brought the broom back into the apartment to wait for the movers. I, it was *I* who caused the disaster that had befallen us when the movers transferred our chattels from New York City to Catatonia!

The movers we chose had assured us of their swiftness, their experience, their honesty, and their reliability. They implied that if we got a head start in our car, they would have all our things out of the New York apartment and into our new home before we got to the Bronx River Parkway.

The van arrived late the *next* afternoon. The men in charge of it explained that the delay had been caused by a breakdown, but, until this moment I am telling about, when I comprehended that all our trouble had been caused by my having moved an old broom, I had regarded that tale about a breakdown as a most feeble excuse. Now, however, my ignorance—my folly—began to explain everything.

The more I pondered the matter, the surer I was that it *had* to be the broom. How else could two double- and three single-bed sheets have been removed from a sealed carton? How else could two or three phonograph records, from various albums, have disappeared into thin air? One leg was missing from our big bed, and the leg was nowhere to be found; three cups and two saucers and a divided vegetable bowl were missing from what had been a complete set of unmatchable antique china; *two* legs were gone from our most comfortable chair; and various pieces of upholstery were slit in various places.

But now the mystery was solved, as well as the mystery of why one thing after the other had gone wrong with us ever since we set foot in Catatonia—*that broom was still in the house!* Knowing at last in which direction I had to proceed, I jumped up from the floor and raced into the basement. There it was, trying to fool me by looking as innocent as any well-disposed broom. Now that I knew it for what it was, I had to force myself to reach out for it—but I did. I grabbed it up and tried to break it across my knee, desisting only when it became obvious at once that I was breaking my knee and not the broom. Telling myself to remain calm, I went about the job in a saner, steadier fashion. I hunted for our axe, found it, and within five minutes had the remains of the broom blazing in the incinerator outside.

Now life, escaped from that cloud, could begin again.

I returned to the kitchen, made breakfast for the girls, and rejected the urge to get to the dishes. Almost without knowing it, I began to work up a new fit of antagonism against the insurance company which had promised to repay us for any damage to our belongings while they were being moved. Eight months and twelve letters had elapsed since we first presented our claim, and still nothing had been done about it.

Telling the girls that I had something important I had to take care of, I promised them untold wealth and pleasure if they would but grant *me* the untold wealth and pleasure of an hour's quiet. They sweetly agreed, and I was gratified to see that getting rid of that broom had already resulted in a change for the better. I left a note on the kitchen bulletin board to buy a new broom, and, in a mood of confidence, decided to write a final communication to the insurance company—one that would be bound to produce results.

Getting out my typewriter, I set about searching for a pad of typewriter paper I had bought a few days before. After fifteen minutes, the search led me to Jennie. If clean white paper gave off the same impulses as uranium, Jennie would be priceless as a Geiger counter. I appealed to her sense of honesty and fair play by giving her two minutes to return my paper, whereupon she dived to the bottom of her filing system and, with one and a half minutes to spare, she surfaced with what was left of my property. All but the bottom six pages of it were covered with rabbits, kittens, gnomes, puppies, ballerinas, and (lucky for her) notations like: "I love my mother."

Sending Jennie on her way, I sat down at the typewriter and composed, for the insurance company, the following questionnaire:

Please fill in proper blanks to indicate why claim has been ignored for eight months? Please?

1. We hate you and will never pay you_____.

2. It is necessary that you get 10____20____ 30____more competitive bids and use your precious time interviewing____more furniture repairmen.

3. You must make____more calls to our man in Philadelphia____; Seattle____; Wiscasset____; other____; and ask him what's the matter.

4. We have fired another man in Toledo____; Walla Walla____; Bergen____; Norfolk____; and the movers have smashed up another van in____(?), and it will take another 8____, 10____, 15____months to get back to____, 18 your problem.

5. Your moving company is so busily occupied in juggling different loads and delaying promised arrivals and giving away boxes of clothing, china, phonograph records, and linens to the wrong people that they can't take the time to give us the necessary papers to complete payment of your claim.

6. You are a Democrat____. You are a Republican____.

7. Go hammer on water____ .

Reading my composition over, I was filled with a glow of creative reward. But gradually a more sober view set in, based largely on the fact that corporations are not noted for their sense of play, and in the end, putting the questionnaire aside, I wrote the conventional "Dear Sir, I would appreciate your immediate attention" letter. Then I addressed an envelope and started to fold the letter into it, when I became intrigued with a conversation the girls were having in the living room. Often, I listen in on their chats, not eavesdropping, just enjoying and hoping to learn something. The week before, I had gained information on copyright laws and the location of Portugal by listening in on one of their discussions. (There is no such thing as an eternal, everlasting copyright—you can't take it with you, and you can't even leave it where you want it; not forever, anyhow. Portugal is a country, not a city, and is sort of swirled around the bottom of Spain. It is not a city down there in South America, somewhere around Brazil and Mexico, as I'd thought.)

On this morning, their conversation went something like this:

Jennie: I wonder why people's veins get big when they grow old.

Miranda: Oh, it's just a habit.

Jennie: Yeah, I guess so. Look, Miranda; here's a good, big magazine we can put under the paper while we color it.

Louise: (In a whisper that could have been heard in Jackson Heights) S-s-s-t! I counted the money we saved and guess what? We have enough for a bottle of perfume! We can get her an ounce of Toujours Moi.

Jennie: An *ounce?* An ounce, an ounce, an ounce! Do you know how much that is? That's about a spoonful— that's what an ounce is! That might be all right for a *friend,* but your own mother! A nice, middle-aged lady like that? We should buy her a quart, at least a quart, of Toujours Moi!

The sound of a brief scuffle indicated that Louise was making a real effort to set the younger girls straight on the facts of life regarding perfume. An agreement was reached and order restored before I found it necessary to enter the arena. For this, I was thankful; I didn't want the girls to know I had overheard their plan to surprise me. Louise went back to reading *Little Women* and Jennie and Miranda returned to their crayoning project and the discussion of other subjects. Soon they began talking about nationalities—I heard Jennie tell Miranda that I was Irish, but that they (the girls) and Hank were French. At this, I deserted my business papers and sprinted up the steps and into the living room. Seldom, if ever, did I get a chance to tell the girls anything they didn't know, and I didn't intend to give Louise time to beat me to the draw. It took me but a few minutes to explain that we were all Americans, and that where our ancestors came from was interesting, but not important. I was about to return to the dining room when Miranda asked: "Is France in Washington? Is that why Daddy talks French to his mother and father when we're there?"

"No," said Louise, detaching herself again from the doings of the March family, "it's a country in——"

"Stop intering up, Louise," said Miranda.

"Yes," I said, "stop intering up, Louise."

"You mean, 'interrupting,'" said Jennie.

I closed my eyes, breathed deeply, counted to four, and answered: "Let's start over. I just came up here to say that we're all Americans. And France, Miranda, is a country in Europe. That's all." I turned to leave and then Louise said, "The French nation has produced some of our greatest writers."

Of course, I felt it necessary to agree and, further, to point out that all countries had produced great literary figures. In the interests of simple justice, I mentioned the names of Sean O'Casey, James Joyce, George Bernard Shaw, and a few other Irishmen. Planning to bring my little lecture to a close, I took a poetry anthology from the bookshelf, with the thought of reading to the girls one of William Butler Yeats' poems. The book fell open, as it always did, on the page containing "The Lake Isle of Innisfree."

I read:

I will arise and go now, and go to Innisfree,
And a small cabin build there, of clay and wattles made;
Nine bean rows will I have there, a hive for the honey bee,
And live alone in the bee-loud glade.

Reading the verses, I found myself filled with the same vague nostalgia, mixed with the same sense of sweet peace, that I get from reading that poem and from nothing else, no matter how grand. Ever since I first read it, when I was only eleven years old, I have had a longing for such a place as Innisfree. I have believed that if I found myself in a place where "midnight's all a glimmer, and noon a purple glow, and evening full of the linnet's wings," I would ask nothing more from life.

Then, as if from a great distance, Miranda's voice came to me. I heard her say, "Mommy, *Mommy!* I thought you didn't *like* bees!"

Under the spell of the poem still, detached and dreaming, I put my arms around her and said: "Ah, but me darling, 'tis not the wicked, wild, waspish things in this place that call themselves 'bees' you'd be finding in Innisfree. Sure, in all of Ireland, there's not a bit of a thing would do you harm. No flies, no mice, and no snakes—ever since the day when St. Patrick drove them all out of the green, glorious land . . ."

Louise said, "St. Patrick wasn't born in Ireland. Nobody knows where he came from; some say England."

Rudely thrust out of my dream world, I turned to her and thundered, "WHO'S IRISH? YOU OR ME?"

"You said none of us was," she answered.

I don't know, honestly, how I was drawn into it, but soon I was declaiming on things Hibernian—all the way from High King Brian Boru and his victory at Clontarf in 1014 A.D. to Victor Herbert. About the only thing I didn't do was sing "Mother Machree"; I can't swear that I wouldn't have if the girls hadn't made it quite clear, finally, that it was time for lunch.

I hastened to put my insurance-company letter into its envelope, sealed it, and ran out to put it in the mailbox to be picked up by the postman. All the while I was engaged in this business and fixing lunch, I was castigating myself. "I'd like to direct your attention to another work of Mr. Yeats'," I said to myself, "one called 'Cap and Bells.'" What would you think of Hank if he should go on about 'Marianne' as you did about 'Cathleen ne Houlihan'!"

The next day I bought a new broom, which by the end of the week was looking just like the old one but apparently carried no curse, for on the following Monday we got a letter from the insurance company. The letter, which thanked me for mine, enclosed a check in settlement of our claim. Getting the check made me feel as jaunty as a top hat, as triumphant as a cock crow. It wasn't the money—that was just something to be fought over by the oil-burner man and the furniture repairman —what caused my jubilation was that receiving the check proved to me, conclusively, that our long spell of hard luck had been broken, destroyed in the flames with the evil broom.

When Hank drove up to the house that evening, he found me outside, where I was waiting for him and gleefully waving the check. At first Hank was as delighted as I that the insurance company had finally paid up, but after a few moments he looked at me and asked, "What did you say in that letter? Must have been pretty stern—was it?"

"Why, no," I answered. "It was just like all the others

I've been writing to them." To prove that it was, I went to look for the carbon I had made and kept.

I found the carbon. Also the original. What I *didn't* find was the questionnaire—and it was then I realized that it was the questionnaire I had mailed, not the letter. For a few moments I was embarrassed. But almost immediately it became quite clear to me that everything hinged on the broom, and on my superstitions. If I hadn't annihilated the broom, would I have been lucky enough to make such a mistake?

## 9

"Aren't the schools closed on Friday?" Hank asked, one night in late September. "How about coming to town for the day? You can take one of the morning trains and meet me for lunch."

"I'll call Gladys right now!" I said. "Even if I have to wake her up. I'm not giving you a chance to change your mind."

School being closed meant that Gladys, a neighborhood girl of eighteen who was a senior in high school, would be free on Friday. In Gladys we had found a

gentle, kind girl whom the children loved, who enabled
me to leave the house with almost complete peace of
mind. Although she sounded sleepy when she answered
the phone, Gladys said she would be glad to sit on
Friday. That night I didn't worry—not even about
Sherman Adams. What kept me awake was excitement
and anticipation! I had been afraid I wouldn't get back
to New York before they had torn down the new
Guggenheim Museum.

Friday arrived, and with it Gladys, right on time.
She kept the children entertained by teaching them how
to make paper roses, while I dressed. I knew it was
going to be one of my good days, because according
to Stephanie's Statute (or, if you will, Lamont's Law),
the woman happy is the woman attractive; i.e., a bride,
even wearing a crash helmet, is beautiful. Once I was
in my high heels and the black sheath that had been
hanging in the closet patiently waiting for this day, I
felt like saying, "Move over, Monte Cristo—the world
*was* yours."

The girls were speechless, momentarily, when they beheld the change in me. Miranda was particularly awed.
I suppose she wondered how I had grown, suddenly,
so tall, among other things. Her memory couldn't stretch
to the point where she had last seen me dressed up.
Jennie kept yelling, "Mama! Mama! You look just like
a TEA-NAJER!" Louise was more contained; she merely
smiled her approval. Woman to woman.

When the taxi drove up, we all waved and cried
good-bye. I promised to return with gifts—and Daddy—

99

and then I was off. We made what the real estate people describe as a "ten-minute ride to the station" in fifteen minutes flat, due to the taxi's average speed of eighty miles an hour, taking every corner on two wheels. Almost paralyzed with fright, I longed to ask the driver to take it easy, but feared that if I betrayed my alarm he might add to it.

By design, I arrived at the station with at least half an hour to spare. Even though the train was almost always late, I was taking no chances. I had heard that once it arrived a full twenty minutes *early,* and had taken off immediately. Those who arrived in good time, and had planned to take that train, were forced to wait three hours before the next iron horse got there. Stage-coaching must have had its points.

During the endlessness of the half-hour wait, which was a bit like the endlessness of half-past three in the morning, I hoped, with the dim hope of all who yearn for the impossible, that for this one time I would be spared a Talker. This is one of my curses—at the movies, on busses, trains, and subway cars; in restaurants and everywhere, actually, that people congregate, it is my fate to fall among Talkers. It could be that the trouble is not that there are so many Talkers as that I am a Hearer. But how can you avoid hearing them—people who converse at the top of their lungs?

Standing on the platform, waiting for the train, I made myself a promise—this time I'll really case the train. No sitting in a car with screaming children running up and down the aisle while their mothers ingest the

latest, biggest best-seller and try to look as though they
were totally unacquainted with their tots. And no sitting
in any car where anyone even *seems* to know his seat
companion.

A stir among the waiting passengers indicated that
the train had begun to take shape in the distance.
Marvellous! Only fifteen minutes late today. Progress!
On to the moon! When the train stopped, I mounted
the steps, went into one of the cars, and found it to be
nearly empty. No children, only a sprinkling of women,
and a few men—some looking glazedly out the windows,
some deep in newspapers. Pretty good. I wasn't likely
to do any better than this.

The place I selected was behind a seat occupied by
two men who seemed unrelated and in front of two
dignified, middle-aged ladies who appeared unaware of
each other. The train labored, it moved, and it was
true—I was on my way to Manhattan. For a whole, whole
day, I would be back in my lovely city, with nothing
to do but walk up and down, and simply *be* there. Let's
face it, I thought. New York is where I belong.

My blissful anticipations of the day ahead were cut
short, suddenly and cruelly, by one of the stately ladies
behind me. She uttered a massive throat-clearing and
asked her companion:

"Hev youah evah stedd with Mestah Rubbins on
Swiggams Lot?"

Clear and loud as Big Ben on New Year's Eve came
the reply: "Frim tame to tame. Yis."

And then there was a silence. Gradually I relaxed,

as long minutes went by and I heard nothing more. But I should have known better. And after several villages dashed by, I did know better, as the first lady trumpeted:

"Veddy clevah chaild."

"Veddy."

Another long silence. Several towns later, I winced at the throat-clearing again and braced myself for:

"*Both* the fathah and the mothah ahe Ph.D.'s, y'know. Place is filthy, of couhse."

I said to myself, "Coo, ducks, we 'ave 'ad it, 'aven't we! Never turn it up, they won't." I got to my feet and struggled against the sway of the ancient car to the door. It's always been an uneven contest between me and train doors—me against more than my weight in steel and pneumatic controls—but I threw myself into the struggle with a will, and finally made it.

It became abundantly obvious, the instant I reached the next car, that here was not the hoped-for haven either. A young woman was yelling at her companion, ". . . because what it takes is nine months and if your friend had a baby in seven she must not be a full human bean *she* must be part *mammal* that's all I got to say. . . ." I knew it was not all she would have to say. She would not hit a period all the way to New York. Seeing that it would be folly to remain, I lurched on, locked wills with two more doors, and then, too tired to go on, sank down in the first vacant seat in the next car.

Fortunately, it was practically empty. There was a little old lady up front, a large, middle-aged gentleman sound

asleep a few seats behind her, a nice-looking girl reading a newspaper, and me. Peace. I looked out of the window at the houses, the filling stations, the main streets flying by, and gave myself up to the knowledge that in about fifteen minutes I would be in New York.

Suddenly the train went into a series of jetés as formidable, if not as graceful, as any of Nijinsky's, and stopped. Two conductors rushed through the car; I could hear a bang and a clatter as they opened the outside doors and left their posts of duty. No one in the car seemed to have noticed. I turned to the window, wondering what dire calamity had happened, and there, not more than ten feet away, spelled out on a sign in huge red letters, the calamity was.

## WARNING! DANGER! HIGH VOLTAGE! KEEP AWAY!!! THIS MEANS YOU!!

Bet your life it means me, I thought. And then, as the hideous realization dawned: "Oh dear God! What is going to become of the children? This is the end. Some of that voltage must have fallen right across the tracks, and this might as well be the death house in Sing Sing. Is there nobody but me who knows, or *cares*, that we are doomed? Those trainmen know all right. You didn't see them lingering—they've run off to let us die here like rats in a trap. . . . Stop it, stop it," I said. Trying to resist hysteria, to face the end bravely like Sydney Carton, I whispered, ". . . far, far greater rest

I go to—oh, no, please! I'm not all that tired——" I sat
with my teeth clenched, fists squeezed, and a blind of
terror behind my eyes, waiting for the flash that would
reduce us all to ashes.

Nothing happened. And nothing continued to happen.
I unclamped my jaws, opened my fists, and felt the blind
of terror lift from my eyes. Gradually I gained enough
confidence to open my handbag and steathily feel around
for the little packet of lucky coins, battered rabbits' feet,
and various other charms. During the next hour, while
the extension of nothing continued to happen, I sat still
and clutched the packet. Then, as the middle-aged man
who was sleeping began to snore, the trainmen—bright
as crickets, merry, indeed, as grigs—returned, slammed
the doors, and the train started to move.

Thus it was that approximately two and one-half hours
after leaving home, I arrived in Manhattan. I found a
telephone booth and called Hank to explain why I had
missed our lunch date. Lord, men are peculiar! There I
was—hungry, disappointed, and still able to see that
ghastly sign, and Hank went off into a tirade about all
the bad experiences *he* had had on the train. I
sympathized with him until he felt better, went to the
ladies' room, and fixed myself up a little.

The results were cheering. My good little dress had
withstood the rigors of the journey better than I. It was
made of sterner stuff. I bought myself a quick lunch
in the coffee shop of one of the hotels that you can
enter from Grand Central, and reminded myself to pick
up some trifles for the girls before leaving the station.

I remembered what happened when I returned home from a shopping trip, years before, with no presents.

Believing that Louise and Jennie (we just had the two girls then) would be spoiled by an abundance of presents, I had firmly resisted all puzzles, candies, toys, and books, and had returned home with not a gift, but a necessity. Jennie needed some slippers, and the ones I chose must have seemed like a present, having bunnies on the toes. Carefully, I explained to both children, when I gave Jennie the slippers, that they were not a gift. I adjured Louise not to feel slighted, because she *had* slippers. Louise had nodded gravely and agreed. The whole subject was then dropped. This scene took place around eleven o'clock in the morning, and when Hank got home that evening, around six, he said, "Hello, Louise." And Louise answered, "Oh, nothing. Jennie just got a new pair of slippers, that's all. I'd rather go barefoot."

From that day forward, I never went home from an expedition without a separate but equal trinket for each child. "All right," I said, bringing my attention back to lunch. "Finish the coffee and get three chocolate pencils in Schrafft's and then forget the girls. This is your day—what's left of it."

## 10

When I got out onto busy, noisy Forty-second Street, I found myself smiling. I walked up to Madison, turned, and continued uptown to Forty-eighth Street and then went east to Park Avenue. Without my telling them to, my feet had fallen back into that brisk stride that all New Yorkers seem to have. Gratefully, I inhaled the perfume of that poisonous air, and delighted in the awesome racket. I was so full of love for this most wonderful city, this *only* city, that I yearned to kiss someone—anyone.

At Park and Forty-eighth, I couldn't stand not knowing what was happening at Madison and Forty-seventh, so I cut back to Madison, and walked downtown to Forty-sixth, feeling full of good will and fondness and joy. "Hello, Abercrombie & Fitch. Hello, Crouch & Fitzgerald. Hello, New York. Hello. Oh, I've *missed* you." I turned west and walked up Forty-fifth Street and there, just past the corner of Forty-fifth and Madison, a group of mailmen was standing near a couple of trucks. It was hard to keep from smiling at them—too hard, so I smiled at them. "Hello, lovely mailmen," I wanted to say. "Hello, lovely mail trucks."

A taxi swished by, going east, and someone in it whistled loudly. Joy? Be still my soul, be still. We just got ourselves whistled at! Three children, a Himalaya of dishes, a sea of soapsuds vaster than the wild Atlantic, and we just got whistled at. Hello, New York, and thank you!

Just then, one of those lovely mailmen appeared at my side and said, "Excuse me. There's a gentleman in a taxi waiting for you, back there at the avenya. He asked me to get you. Said he whistled, but I guess you didn't hear him? Says his name's King."

Jake! Jake King! I thanked the mailman and hastened back to Madison, so glad to be meeting Jake that I didn't even mind the fact that the whistle I got wasn't a real wolf whistle. Jake King is a little, dark, ugly man who runs one of the most successful model agencies in New York City. I met him when I was sent to him by an employment agent who described him as a "top-flight"

type in need of a "top-flight" stenographer. One look at
me and Jake told me with rough kindness that he needed
a more experienced hand (he meant more intelligent).
I was turning to leave, trying to hide my disappointment
at having failed to land a job again, when Jake said:
"Hold on," and I held on, and listened, with the result
that when I left his office, it was to begin a brief career
in modeling, instead of stenography. (Not a career,
really, but I was employed fairly steadily as the wholesome, junior type during the years it took me to meet,
woo, and wed Hank.)

Jake was self-educated, self-made, and totally self-
effacing. And I, along with many others, was in his debt
not only for the job, but for uncountable small and not-
so-small favors; the loan between paydays, impatient but
accurate advice on how to get along in the Big City, the
right kind of clothes to wear, the type of men to avoid.
He should only happen to everybody!

When I reached his cab, Jake was holding the door
open. I jumped in with a big, warm hello, as Jake gave
me one of his quick, cold, appraising glances.

"Good," he said. "You look good. The sticks must
agree with you? So how's the family? Or *do* the sticks
agree with you? You've lost weight—and your cheekbones, they're a little higher, no?"

"Never mind me and my cheekbones," I said. "What
about you? You look fine. How are you really, though?"

He ignored my question, and continued, "At that, the
sticks is better than Africa. Now aren't you glad I didn't
let you marry that what's-his-name, was gonna open up

the radio station in the Transvaal? Imagine you—Mrs. Marconi of the Veldt!"

"Come on now, Jake. Don't start that again. I never was going to marry what's-his-name, anyway. Hank says you've been in Europe. How was it?"

"For Europeans, Europe is a great place. For me, I like it here. How much you weigh now? You look good, being a little more skinny. Kids give you exercise, eh? Lemme see you in profile."

"Oh, stop it!" I answered. "This is *me*."

"I don't know it? Can I buy you a drink? I'll tell you how I fell into the Seine. Biggest commotion in Paris since the Liberation."

"I'd love to have a drink with you, Jake. But all I really want to do is walk. I'm afraid I might miss something."

"OK. Better I should skip the drink myself. I got to defend myself this afternoon against a lot of mamas who all think the circulation of every magazine in the country will fall off if their little girls ain't on the next ten covers. You know—and a little child shall feed them. Dizzy as you are, I'd rather walk with you, if I didn't hate to walk. Where do you want to start?"

I asked him to let me out at Fifth Avenue and Fifty-seventh Street (all of a sudden I felt I must know what was happening there), and when the cab pulled up to the curb, I exorcised my impulse to kiss somebody by kissing Jake. "Dizzy," he said. "Dizzy, first prize. Watch where you're walking. Don't forget you ain't in the sticks. So long, apple-knocker. Listen: I'll save you a little shoe leather; you don't have to check the lions at the library. They're still there."

Jake went on his way—just like him, I thought, to go out of his *way*—we must ask him for dinner after we get the place fixed up a little. And as soon as I can look this happy there . . . I looked into Bergdorf's for a while and then crossed over to see what Bonwit's had to offer. Slowly now, instead of briskly, I began to stroll uptown, savoring every step, looking into the windows of the odd little shops that I always think of as being tucked into the pockets of the big Manhattan stores. Eventually, I came to my favorite spot of all—Central Park, in front of the Plaza Hotel: the fountain, the trees of the park, the coachmen, the hacks, the horses snuffling in their nose bags. Hello, horses; hello, coachmen; hello, you beautiful fountain. As soon as the girls are old enough, I thought, we must bring them down here for another ride around the park in the carriage with the coachman and the horse; I'll bet Miranda has forgotten she ever had a ride around Central Park.

A bit tired by now, I was tempted to sit on a bench in the park, but what would I miss if I did? I drank in the view, great big draughts of it, and resumed my pilgrimage —the windows of the art galleries on Fifty-seventh Street filled with the poetry of paint, the bookstore windows redolent (even through the glass!) of old leather and wisdom, the antique shops over on Third Avenue where I was, on the instant, rich beyond the dreams of avarice and could afford vast purchases of marble, gilt, glass, and mahogany. And the choicest pieces of the heaps of

111

old, old jewelry spilled inside the windows. I nodded vigorous approval over the lot, in which not a single emerald fly or ruby turtle or diamond bunny was to be found. Time marched, time passed, time flew, and I walked—sometimes congratulating New York on a few of her newest buildings; sometimes commiserating with her on the loss of old ones. Before I knew it, it was five o'clock. Hastening to Hank's office, I found him waiting for me all alone.

"My, Stephanie," he said. "Don't you look lovely!"

Praise from Caesar. Even better than getting whistled at. Hank offered me a cigarette, and as we sat in the relaxed intimacy of a New York office after hours, an intimacy like no other, he said that he had telephoned some old friends, and had asked them to meet us at the Plaza. "But you've already been there, haven't you?" he said. "You've been walking all afternoon." (I have no secrets.) "But that's all right. We can get a cab."

I asked him not to, saying truthfully that I'd rather walk. We left his office and strolled in the direction from which I had come, contentedly untalkative, like two old friends. When we reached the fountain in front of the Plaza, Hank broke the silence. "We're still early," he said. "Let's just sit for a few minutes, shall we?"

No wonder that man and I got married. We found ourselves a bench in the park and watched the lights come on in the dusk and there it all was, spread out before me—my town. After a while, Hank touched my arm.

Without looking, I said to him: "Hank, I know that I

would be low man on anyone's IQ list, but even so, it shouldn't have taken me eight years to understand why Jake was so insistent that I go to that Christmas party." Then I did look at him, and we both smiled, and, "Time to go," he said. And we went off to the Oak Room of the Plaza and met our friends.

## 11

Later in the fall, in October, I found a friend. No, *two* friends. One was a woman, more or less my age, named Maria Canwell. The other was an older lady—much, much older. Well maybe not a lady, but anyway, a woman. She was Mother Nature.

I can't say I was looking for a friend. Not that I didn't long sometimes for what others (with stomachs less delicate than mine) call "girl talk." But, since I knew my limitations, I didn't think that the female population of Catatonia could offer me much in the way of

114

companionship—most of the women I had met so far I'd hesitate to sit beside on a bus, let alone become intimate with. That was my feeling before I met Maria.

Miranda introduced me to Maria one day when she and I had left the house, soon after seeing the older girls off on the school bus. It just so happened that I had to get out of the house that morning. A space man fell out of the cereal box into Jennie's bowl while I was serving breakfast, and there was no use in trying to say to myself, when I screamed in fright, "Just nerves." *Just* nerves! And then, later, when I went to look for Miranda, I heard her talking to someone I couldn't see. "Horace Mossy," she replied, when I asked her who was there in the bedroom with her.

"Who," I asked, "is Horace Mossy?"

"A ghost," she answered.

"What kind of a ghost?"

"Friendly, of course," she said, a bit impatient at the suggestion that she would traffic with any other sort. (Nothing irregular about Miranda!)

Personally, I don't believe in ghosts. I simply persuaded myself that we had to take care of a few pressing matters in town, and it was not Mr. Mossy I wanted to escape, but rather all the committee chairmen who would begin telephoning soon.

We dressed, got a taxi, and went to town, bringing along a skirt of mine about which I wanted to have a few words with the cleaners. During the long drive, with my eyes stricken by the unimaginable beauty of the scenery, I began to have an inkling of why people pre-

115

ferred to live in the country. Not that I shared their preference; not that I wouldn't have traded, promptly, the rioting, roman-candle-like glory of all the oaks, elms, maples, and whatever kind of trees they were, for one dusty, glorious black-and-white Manhattan block. But it is undeniable that Nature as an artist can't be faulted. She may be a miserable housekeeper, letting her plant and animal life run wild, but, certainly, she has a marvelous sense of color. For the first time, I began to appreciate what Corot, Van Gogh, Matisse, and others were trying to say, and how difficult was the task for which they had been chosen.

The taxi let us out at Front Street. (That's Catatonia's main street, the business section. Why it's called that, I don't know. It isn't the front of anything.) The street is just about one hundred and fifty yards long and forty feet wide, and (big deal) the town fathers have even recently discarded dirt sidewalks in favor of concrete ones, and erected a traffic light in the middle of the block.

The traffic light, which is incessantly under repair, is absolutely essential. There is an endless stream of cars racing up and down the road and an interesting thing about them is that, among all the cars, you can search for hours for an American-made auto. The population of Catatonia looks upon driving an unforeign car as almost as cardinal a social sin as using a flower pot as a planter. (I know I'm straying, but there isn't a self-respecting geranium up here that wouldn't rather die than live in anything but an old-time phone, a brass spittoon, an umbrella stand, or a morning-glory radio speaker.)

Miranda and I walked a short way up the block, to the traffic signal. Noting with surprise that it was working today, I decided to chance crossing the street. As soon as the light changed, we ran, but were only halfway across when the light changed (it's some sort of a Russian roulette game, I think). Some wag, some wise-apple in an Isotta, who had become enraged at having to wait the one-tenth of a second that the light was against him, gave us a loud blast of the horn, and roared his motor at us. We sprinted the remaining twenty feet and made it.

We went into a store whose sign proclaimed it as HI-CLASS CLNG & DYING—SATISFACTION, WHAT ELSE? and approached the counter. Behind it, there stood a woman with a seemingly iron bosom and hair the color of mildew. I began to suggest mildly that the zipper they had put in my skirt (which I showed her) might look better if it lay flat in the placket instead of being shirred; that, since the skirt was red, a red zipper might look better than the bright yellow one they had chosen. The lady stood with her arms, shall we say, akimbo, and her eyes fixed on a spot about six feet above my head. At first, I thought she might be blind, but then became convinced she must be watching something really vital, and so my narrative faltered as I turned, irresistibly, to see what merited her close attention. At the same moment, the lady gave tongue, in the voice of Bugle Ann, to:

117

"B—E—R—T!!! Willya c'mout here a minute lady wantsa see ya!" I jumped and turned back to face the counter, where, presently, "Bert" appeared. He gazed at me so piercingly that I was beginning to believe they would have the stocks set up with me locked in them in no time, if I so much as made one false move.

Bert barked: "Yep?"

I repeated my story about the zipper, which even I was starting to think of as a thin tissue of lies. Bert called in another executive and they went into a conference, during which they both cast suspicious glances in my direction and the lady remained fixed, her arms inexorably akimbo, her eyes pinned to the same spot. Eventually, Bert dismissed his colleague, and began to interrogate me. To his grilling, I was forced to admit that I hadn't specified that the zipper should be red, but considered that the color of the skirt was prima facie evidence (if that is the best kind) that it should be. I insisted that it was indeed at his shop that I had left the skirt to be repaired, and that I had not charged the cost of the repair, but had paid the $2.65 in cash. Finally, he agreed to have the job done over, and allowed that the skirt might be ready in a week, ten days; I could stop in then anyway and check, and don't forget the receipt or they wouldn't be responsible.

We left and, heavy-footed, heavy-hearted, went into the Spice of Life Variety Store, next door. Here I wanted to buy some socks for the children, instead of at The Satisfied Child, which dealt, it seemed to me, exclusively in clothes for millionaires' tots. We found the socks counter, with thousands of socks arranged neatly in bins and labeled, "Size 1, 2, 3, 4, 5, 7, 8, 9, 10." Choosing a couple of size fours for Miranda, I began to search for some size sixes for the other girls. There wasn't any size-six bin. There also wasn't any clerk. I spied a bell which bore a placard that exhorted me to "Ring for Service," which I did. After about ten minutes a person, shambling of gait, unfortunate of complexion, and abundant of hip, advanced towards us on green wedgies with runover heels. She was a female of about eighteen summers, but she hadn't been a girl in years. She blew a couple of bubbles with her gum and, fixing her tiny eyes upon me, said, "Yeah?"

"Size six?" I asked.

"Size-six what?"

Reality began to fade. I was practically going down for the third time in a sea of nothing but socks, for heaven's sake, *and* holding a pair in front of her face! What did she think I meant? Size-six snow shovels?

"Socks. Size-six socks."

"Ain't gotny," she riposted, and turned and slouched her way back from whence she had come. To a cave, I presumed.

I dropped the socks I had selected back into their bin, and we left. It's not, I thought, that I expect Japanese lanterns to be strung up in anticipation of my patronage. Still, I resent being given the kind of warm, rousing welcome, roughly, that King Farouk might expect from Gamal Abdel Nasser. Out on the street, I tried smiling at Miranda and said, "Let's get a little snack, and go home, shall we?" She smiled, too, for the first time since

John huchnetgarth

we had left home. We found a luncheonette, and I ordered a couple of hot dogs from a youth who turned and threw two buns and the hot dogs onto a grill without looking up from his comic book. While we were eating, the door opened, Miranda looked up, leaped from her seat, and flung herself, chortling joyfully, upon a lady who had entered the store. The immediate object of Miranda's affection was unknown to me. Once again, I got that lost, eerie feeling that overcomes parents when their children get into the world and start talking to, and about, people their parents have never met, or even heard of.

The lady returned Miranda's greeting not as effusively, but just as affectionately, and they came to join me at the counter. Miranda said: "Mommy, Mommy! My friend, my *friend*, Mrs. Canwell!"

Maria Canwell smiled, held out her hand, and the grayness of the store faded.

"How do you do," said Maria. "I've heard about you from your girls. I met them during story hour at the library. It seems that we're all *Winnie-the-Pooh* fans. They're lovely children."

That did it, that adjective about the girls. She asked if she might join us and we said please do—she ordered a sandwich from the boy and gave him one of her warm, pleasant smiles, saying, "Hi, Herbie; how's your mother?" Before he could answer her, I knew that this woman and I were friends. She lived out past the farthest stretches of Catatonia, where the country is still country. She had an economist husband, a boy at prep school, and she herself, before she married, had taught history at one of the colleges for women in New England. She was warm, she was intelligent, and she was good to look at. She wasn't wearing Bermuda shorts, and her hair, though not untidily long, was not crew-cut.

Maria offered us a ride and invited us to stop first at her house. We accepted, and when I entered her house, I felt a shameful pang of envy. I thought I wouldn't mind living in Catatonia, I might be more like Maria, if I were the mistress of such a house. Of course, it was the other way around. Maria would have lent grace to a pup tent pegged down in the middle of a howling jungle. After a little visit, we went out to see Maria's garden, now abloom with late-fall lovelies: row after row of chrysanthemums and asters in blue, white, bronze, wine, yellow, pink, orange, and purple. Maria said: "These beds are getting awfully overcrowded; I'll have to divide the flowers in the spring. I'd love to give you some, Stephanie. And I've got ground cover, too, that needs thinning out. Come over Saturday—will you have time? We'll dig some up; you won't have to wait for spring to plant the ground cover. Anytime before frost is all right."

"Thank you, but I—I'm sorry! But I wouldn't know how—I don't know the first *thing* about planting——"

Maria grinned. She said, "I'll help you." And when I tried to thank her: "I love to garden and, honestly, most of the fun of it is sharing it."

She gave me a huge bunch of the chrysanthemums and asters, and drove Miranda and me home. After we'd said good-bye, and Maria had left, I went into the house, breathing in great draughts of the cinnamony autumn fragrance of the flowers, and searched for exactly the right container for them, a copper bowl which I polished and rubbed until it shone. When I had filled it with the flowers, I put it on one of the tables, in a shaft of sunlight, and Miranda and I, sitting close together, sat and stared.

When Hank got home that evening, Miranda and I interrupted each other until he got the whole story: about meeting Maria, about the flowers, and how she was going to give me, *me!* some plants! "In the spring, some flowers," I said; "some flowers like these, and right now, what she called *ground cover;* that's a long, viney kind of thing——"

"Myrtle," said Louise. "It must be myrtle. It has a blue flower in the spring. 'Myrtle' is its common name, but it's really 'vinca minor.'"

I gazed at her and replied, kindly, "Why don't you stand up straight? Honestly! Your posture——"

Hank drove me to the library that evening and waited while I raided the shelves on gardening. I didn't worry that night. I read: about how wisteria was named after someone in Owen Wister's family (and I had thought their only claim to fame was *The Virginian*); what greedy feeders begonias are (I did think that was phrased a little tactlessly); how beneficial mulches are; and how to deal with red spider, wilt, and mildew. The next day I called the hardware store, and before you could say "tilth," the grounds outside the house were covered with bales of manure and peat moss, a spreader, pruning shears, an edger, a trowel, and many boxes and bottles of various "cides," to cope with any and all plant enemies. I read the directions for the use of these under a microscope from Jennie's Gilbert Chemical Set (the one remaining unit of a 150-piece outfit) and, gathering from what the manufacturers said that any contact with their products would be fatal, I stored them on a high shelf, against the day when I could afford a lead suit.

On the following Saturday, Maria called for me early in the morning. After we had reached her place, we dug up great quantities of myrtle and pachysandra. She came back to our house with me and showed me how a heavy foot, in planting, is a growing thing's best friend, and all the basic, essential pointers on gardening I needed. We discussed spring-flowering bulbs, and I learned, to my great delight, that daffodils and tulips kept coming up forever, even *multiplying!* How economical, I thought, and after Maria left, I called the hardware store again, and ordered a hundred of each. (After all, some people throw it all away on booze.)

All that day, and on many days thereafter till the frost came, I dug, scratched, and planted. I destroyed quantities of poison ivy, cat briars, and other noxious weeds. And, much as I am embarrassed by whimsy, I have to say that I came to think of Mother Nature not as the slattern as which I had dismissed her, but rather as a poor overworked housewife like myself, who needed only a little help in keeping order.

And a curious thing happened. All the time I was crawling around outside, sweating and filthy from head to foot, I was content. Hours went by, and I didn't want a cigarette or a cup of coffee. I didn't mind the noise the children made while they were outside with me—a racket that would have driven me frantic in the house. I wasn't even annoyed when they helped me with the gardening. And when I went to bed at night, I didn't worry. I slept. One night, after the very best of those days, the last thing I heard as I was drifting off, *before* the children did, was Jennie's voice saying: "Oh, wasn't it a good day! Mommy didn't get mad at us and we almost caught a frog."

That was how it began to be, after I met Maria.

## 12

As the days grew shorter and colder, and we began to smell snow in the air, I reluctantly stored away the gardening gear. This was a difficult operation, as I had been more enthusiastic than prudent in laying in supplies. The basement could barely hold it all. But even though I had to put aside the joys of gardening, I found myself in better spirits than since moving to Catatonia. I had the spring to look forward to, and, in the meantime, I had my friendship with Maria.

One of the many things I appreciated about Maria

was that she called me by my given name—not "Sweetie,"
like Francesca and Blanche; not "Mrs. Uh," like Grazie
and other committee chairmen; and not, naturally,
"Mommy" or "Mama," like Hank and the children. Oh,
Hank sometimes called me Stephanie, but rarely, and
not as he used to before we were married. His way of
using my proper name had become "Ste—PHA—N I E!"
in tones ascendant as a steelworker's pay. It was also
reserved for state occasions, like the time he overheard
me trying to console Jennie, after she had been insulted
by a rude boy on the school bus. "Never mind, Jennie,"
I said. "Tomorrow I'll lay for him at the bus stop, and
we'll see who's the punk. When I get through telling
him——"

"Ste—PHA—N I E!" Hank interrupted, and then added
a number of immaterial comments, ending with, "——absolutely the only grown woman in the *world* who would
fight with a small boy on his own level!" I simply looked
at him. My goodness, on whose level *could* you fight with
a small boy? How unfair to expect me to fight with a small
boy on the level of a grown woman! At any rate, it was
generally at times like this that Hank called me
"Stephanie," or on my birthday. Mostly at home I was
"Mama," and at times I was tempted to point out,
tactfully, that I was not Hank's mama.

I was thinking such thoughts as these on a brilliant
day late in October—a day that Miranda fell so in love
with that she called it the "very *twentiest* of October."
And though I didn't quite know what she meant, it
struck me as being as good a description as any for the

kind of splendor this day wore. For a day off, it was perfect. Hank was going to stay with the children—this very twentiest of October was a Saturday—while I drove out into the country for lunch with Maria. And if I appreciated Maria's calling me Stephanie, I more than appreciated the fact that she understood I could use part of a day off now and then—that two acres, after a week or so of nothing else, can begin to seem like a rather small world.

Maria drove up in her car, and we and my family went through our usual departing ceremony, one that might be thought excessive for such a short absence—much advice from me to Hank on child care, many hugs and kisses from the children, numerous cries of farewell. Maria and I left the house behind, talking easily of books, of boats, of pepper steaks, and if Callas could sing; of poets, dramas, comedy, and almost anything. Eventually, we were driving along a quiet, deserted, country road, and I was mildly curious when Maria stopped the car.

"Stephanie," she said, "how about some driving lessons?"

"Sure, Maria," I replied. "I'd love to learn to drive. Someday."

"Why someday? How about now?"

"*Now?*"

"Why not?"

Maria put it as a question, but it wasn't a question, really. She opened the door on her side of the car and slid from beneath the wheel.

"Maria, wait!" I cried. "Where are you going?"

"Move over," Maria said, coming around to my side of the car. "Take the wheel."

I moved over and took the wheel, but only to gain time. "Listen, just listen, Maria. I *know* I ought to know how to drive. It's ridiculous for me not to. And you know that driving school you told me about? I was thinking that I ought to enroll with them. Actually, I was going to, and would have already, except that I haven't had time. And speaking of time—what about your time! Busy as you are—oh, no, Maria. It would be too much of an imposition! That driving school——"

If someone can look exasperated and amused at the same time, that was the way Maria looked. "Stephanie Lamont, you know and I know that you'll never go near that school. Soon we'll have snow, which will give you another excuse, and by spring you will have thought up a hundred more. So pay attention. This is all you have to do. You turn this key, which controls the switch—go on, turn it."

I did as I was told. Other than get hysterical, there was nothing else I could do. I followed Maria's directions, and then, do you know, the car started and went. And I was driving—*me*, driving—and for all anyone else could tell, just as though I knew how. I almost believed it myself. In another six weeks, after regular Saturday lessons, Maria decided that I had passed all her exacting tests; but we kept my course of instruction a secret from Hank and the girls until I was ready to apply for a license.

Here was another hurdle. Maria believed I could drive, and I was beginning to believe it, too, but would those

who had charge of handing out licenses? I learned that
I would have to pass a test, and that some unknown
man, an officer of the law, would be in the car with
me—watching every move I made. I have never been
good at competitive sports, and I was sure that this
"test" would be just that—a competition between me and
some strange cop, hardly what I'd call sporting. However,
having got this far, I went ahead and wrote, as ingratiat-
ingly as possible, to the motor vehicle bureau, an an-
nouncement that they had another aspirant on their
hands. When the bureau's application for a test arrived,
I displayed it, modestly, to Hank and the girls. That
evening turned into a celebration. Hank called Maria
and her husband, who came to our house. It wasn't until
they arrived that I began to realize that Hank wanted to
convince himself that my being able to drive wasn't
simply something I had dreamed up. Actually, I'm positive
that he wouldn't have believed anybody but Maria (not
even the driving-school people) that I was capable of
handling all that horsepower.

Hank and the girls helped me memorize the rules of
the road, which I learned by heart, soul, and rote. In
time I received another affable (if brief) letter from
the motor vehicle department, this time setting a date
for my test. The licensing bureau in Catatonia is not
open on Saturday (naturally, because that is the only
free day that most of the people living here have), and
this meant that I could not count on Hank's company
during the ordeal. On the whole, I rather thought that
this was just as well. If he saw how nervous I knew I

was going to be, he might change his mind about entrusting the family car to me, regardless of how many tests I passed.

At last, the day arrived. I tensed every muscle to be calm until after breakfast when Hank and the two older girls were out of the house, Hank on his way to work, and the girls on the school bus. Because I needed our car to take the test, Hank was obliged to take a taxi to the station. I looked out at the car in the driveway, and, "For the love of Mike," I said. "Don't blow a gasket, today of all days; although, probably I will." I debated whether I should take a sedative (would it make me too dopey?) or something stimulating (would it make me jittery, *more* jittery?). At last I compromised. I swallowed two aspirins and drank a cup of coffee, hoping for a neutralizing effect.

Alone with Miranda, I awaited the emergence of my better, stronger self—the one I had come to depend upon in times of crisis: such times as when one of the girls got hurt, or when hurricane warnings came over the radio. Let trouble come—real trouble—and she would be there. I could retire while she took over. I knew she had to save her strength, but it didn't seem too much to ask of her to come forward now and pass the driver's test.

I was still waiting for her to show some sense of obligation and loyalty when Maria arrived. In Hank's absence, she had taken it upon herself to drive me, in our car, to the office of the motor vehicle bureau. We left Miranda at the home of a neighbor, one whose children were often left with me.

We reached the motor vehicle bureau, and Maria
parked the car. There, I was terrified to discover that
I had the same desire to flee that overtook me when I
went to see the doctor just before Louise was born. This
doctor's office was in the hospital, and when I had visited
him for what I expected to be another check-up, he
(all horrible smiles) had told me to go right upstairs
to my room. I pretended to accede to his astonishing
demand, and then I got dressed and ran away. I fled
in a taxi, back to the apartment, Hank, and safety. And
outside the motor vehicle bureau, I felt the same urgent
need to escape. I fully confess that I would have, had
it not been for one plain, incontrovertible fact. That fact
was that Maria, traitorous as Hank on that other occasion,
would do exactly as he had done. She would make me
come right back. Since it was inevitable, I went into the
building with Maria.

To discover that I was the only person among some
twenty applicants who was over sixteen—*way* over sixteen—did not add to my sense of confidence. There were
two police officers to take care of the applicants. One
of them was talking to a rather nervous youth, in a
manner that made me glad I wasn't in the boy's shoes—
the best thing you can say for the policeman's manner
was that it was harrowing. The second policeman was
a tremendous improvement. He seemed kind and polite,
one of the avuncular breed of officer. He was speaking
softly, even dulcetly, to a dewy maiden of less than
seventeen happy years. "I hope I get him," I thought.
"He's nice." And it was he, the dear, polite man, that I

did get. Immediately, he became as tough as his fellow officer who had been interrogating the boy. And that one—why now *he* was being understanding, gentle, and cooing-of-voice, to another delightful, dewy maiden, who, if you ask me, looked too young for a scooter.

My inquisitor began asking me questions, suspiciously—far more questions than he had asked that pretty girl —and the whole affair got me so mad that I forgot to be nervous. He asked the questions, and I answered right back. Before I knew it, that part of the test was over. My friend then tested my eyes. He did everything but take them out of my head, looking for I know not what. Eventually, he was forced to admit, unwillingly, that I could see, that I knew the answers to his questions, and that I wasn't too old, yet, to drive.

Then we went out to the car, to the real fun. The curtain-raiser was that I couldn't find the keys. I looked through my purse, my pockets; I scrabbled through the glove compartment of the car. I searched the floor, and was about to conclude that Maria had the keys, when my companion, who all this time had been posed beside me in an attitude of pseudo-patience, suggested, "Why don't you look on the dashboard? The keys are in the switch."

I prayed for the day when he would be on trial for his life. I saw myself as the surprise star witness for the prosecution, brought forth just as the defendant was smugly confident of acquittal. To make my victory unequivocally, deliciously, rapturously complete, I hoped that he would never have *seen* the victim of the crime of which he had been accused. Forced to admit that this happy sequence of events would probably not transpire, I settled for wishing I could give him a kick in the pants. So in an even, pleasant tone I said, "Thank you," turned the key, and put the car into reverse.

The policeman said, "Don't you look behind you when you want to reverse?" To prove that I did, I looked behind me, shifted into drive, and slammed on the brakes just in time. Otherwise, we would have gone clear through the stone wall that the car was facing. I turned off the ignition. I held up my chin. I looked calm.

"OK," said my mentor. "Let's start all over. Pull yourself together. Don't be nervous."

On the instant, I stopped looking calm and started to look the way I felt—angry. "All right!" I thought. "The hell with this. Let's stop trying to impress this peeler and get this thing over with." I started over again, following Mr. Know-It-All's instructions. In due time, after a brief tour of the neighborhood, we returned to our departure point with no visible damage to the officer, me, or the car. As I was reaching to turn off the motor, my mentor said:

"What did you forget?"

"Nothing!" I snapped. "I'M GOING TO PUT ON THE HAND BRAKE RIGHT NOW!"

The officer did not reply at first. He sat meditating as I yanked at the hand brake and sat back. I could remember almost nothing of what I had been doing; my driving had been an entirely mechanical performance. The officer spoke.

135

"Little more practice and you might be a halfway decent driver," he said. "Some day. Gotny kids?"

"I—have—three—little—*girls*," I answered, glacially.

The policeman sat silent again. I waited to be told when I might be allowed to reapply for a license, vowing that when the time came I would ask for a change of venue, on the grounds of prejudice.

"OK," the policeman said. "Don't forget who's responsible for the lives of those kids, those *girls*—" (as I glared) "—when they're in the car, and you're driving. Come on in now, and they'll give you your license."

Having anything but a poker face, I couldn't hide my bliss or my admiration for this splendid pillar of the law. Inside the office, he shook hands with me and offered his congratulations. The trivial business of the fee was taken care of, and I had a license. I could drive; the proof was in my hand. It said in print that I could drive. Maria and I picked up Miranda and went home, and as soon as Maria left in her own car, I called Hank in New York. Do you think for one minute that Columbus wouldn't have telephoned back to Spain if he'd had the chance?

Louise and Jennie came home from school, and I liked their being proud of me; and shortly thereafter, our good Gladys came over. She had agreed to stay with the girls while I made my first solo flight. I wanted to go down to the station alone, by myself, to meet Hank. So excited was I by the prospect that I hardly noticed that Gladys seemed to have more charges than she had bargained for. Each of the girls seemed to have about four playmates apiece; it was very children out and they indulged in much whispering, many suppressed squeals, and a great deal of airy darting about. The same air of secrecy sat on Gladys. Too elated to think of much besides my own stunning accomplishment, I decided that they were probably making plans for Hallowe'en.

When the time came for me to leave, I called good-bye, and in my concern with the task at hand, I but dimly perceived that I wasn't getting my usual abundance of farewells from the girls. They just waved, standing next to Gladys, and disappeared. I started the car, backed up to turn around (carefully looking behind me) and then drove down the hill and onto the road. I proceeded bravely, and also slowly, and just before I reached a little side road that winds around our land, I saw a troop of children, gathered at the junction of the side road. They were dancing, shouting, and waving their arms. Their voices rang out sweet and clear, calling, "Hooray for Mama! Hooray for Mrs. Lamont! Hooray for Miranda's mama! Hooray!" As I drove past, they pelted the car with autumn leaves and with artificial flowers they had spent the afternoon making. Gladys, pink with excitement, delighted at seeing the triumph of her conspiracy, had as much joy out of it as the children. I had more.

## 13

Three weeks before Christmas, I was sitting at the dining-room table, making out lists. They were complex and each one required a separate sheet of paper: Santa to Miranda, Santa to Jennie, Santa to Louise. (That was three lists, already.) Jennie to Daddy, Miranda, Louise. Miranda to Daddy, Jennie, Louise. Louise to Daddy, Jennie, Miranda. And so on. Nobody was missing but Tinker to Evers to Chance. These lists *did not include all the relatives and friends,* nor did they hint at where the money was coming from. I positively refused to face the truth, which was that if we spent about a nickel on each person, we probably could afford something for everyone.

The children were in the living room watching a late-afternoon TV show. This program was one all mothers had heartily welcomed when it replaced an unbearably noisy show, but it had turned out to be just as bad. Jennie's interest was captured by the latest commercial suggestion of the program's master of ceremonies (between these suggestions, the program offered some brief entertainment). Guilelessly, she danced down to me, obeying the man like a good girl:

"You know, Mama," she said, "this year I think we should write Santa to put a Friendship Candy Bar in the toe of our stockings instead of an orange. This bar comes in three parts, and it's only a dime, and there is enough for the child and two of his friends! Isn't that a nifty idea?"

I smiled agreeably, but noncommittally, and she returned to learn of more ways of spending money. As soon as she was out of hearing, I muttered:

"I wish *you* had a friend at Chase Manhattan Bank. Boy, nothing to do but watch TV and lose a couple of dollars' worth of barrettes every week! Friendship Bar, indeed! There isn't enough in those ten-cent candy bars to make a good penny candy. When I was a child, you could get a candy bar for a nickel, and it would last all week!" (I didn't say any of this to her face because sarcasm is wasted on children. Another household hint.)

Returning my attention to the lists, I saw that the

most expensive items had been entered as presents due from Santa Claus. This afforded me much relief till I remembered that there was no Santa Claus. I pulled myself back to reality, and began to check the girls' letters to Santa, to make sure that nothing had been left off the sheets headed "Santa to——" This was Jennie's letter:

"Dear Santa: I want a doll that doesn't do anything."

That was, is now, and always will be, my favorite.

I had already resolved that we would do all our shopping in Catatonia that year. I yearned to see The Windows: Bergdorf Goodman's, B. Altman's fairyland, and even Lord and Taylor's (though *they* would probably have black holly). And to see The Tree at Rockefeller Center. But going to Manhattan meant less money to spend on gifts, so I comforted myself by planning "next year, when the children are older, and we can all go together for the day."

Turning to the "from me to——" list, I closed my mind firmly against the knowledge of what we could afford, and decided "yes" to all the things I wanted to give Hank and the children. Then I allowed myself to think, briefly, about the very small hope—one I hardly allowed to breathe—that this was the year the family was going to give me a dishwasher. I couldn't see where the money was to come from, but I thought that, just possibly, Hank had sold an article—though when could he have found the time? Perhaps he had stayed in during lunch hours, and written it at the office. I hadn't dared, really, to let the hope grow. Still, Jennie had intimated that

I would be getting something that would help me do my housework, and there had been many private conversations between the girls and their father.

Then too, Louise and Jennie had been doing something very secret with Maria—who, in the three weeks before Christmas, had generously had them at her house every afternoon, ever since the "very important letter" had arrived from Hank's mother. "Very important, Mommy, and very personal; so please don't forget to give it to us when it comes!" The only sadness of this whole season was caused by Louise's having arrived at the age which heralded her future independence. She had addressed and signed all her own Christmas cards, and was writing her own letters. I was proud, but couldn't deny a slight wistfulness over the fact that she was no longer completely dependent upon her parents.

The three weeks went by quickly and it was the day before Christmas, surely the best day in all the year. We are very old-fashioned about Christmas. Not for us the bleak decorations suggested in the smarter magazines —the driftwood with the chaste string of pearls, or the one staid, inviolate, prissy gold star on the mantel. We pull out all the stops. Outside, we have a crèche populated by dolls and a big fir tree strung with colored lights. Inside, there is not a square inch that is not festooned and garlanded.

In the early days of our marriage, it was our custom to spend all our Christmases at Hank's parents' house, in Washington, D.C., until the year when Louise, then two, caught a cold from a careless little boy, and we had to stay home. Since we had planned to go to Washington as usual, we had shipped all the presents, eaten all the food in the apartment, and packed our clothes. We unpacked, and poor Hank ran all day and part of Christmas Eve from drugstore to ten-cent store to grocer to butcher. The results were pathetic: a small, scrawny tree with about three ornaments, weird little toys, an indifferent dinner. Realizing that you can't make plans when you have children (is that an understatement!), we had resolved to spend Christmas at home from then on. But we missed the grandparents, who add so much to the festivities. I particularly missed being with Hank's family, in their home, because it was there that I first heard French Christmas carols and grew to love them. I wished we knew some of them, had even rebuked Hank for not having learned the words so he could teach them to us.

During the years following the "poor" Christmas, I had concentrated on collecting Christmas decorations, and had accumulated many dazzling baubles. Besides, we had lots of surprisingly attractive ornaments the girls made at school (smarmy little angels with half-circle mouths, paper chains, stars, tiny trees made of gilded cones). And wonder of wonders! We owned an artificial tree, three feet high, trimmed with real ermine tails. This was a present from Jake, and I loved it, although it was absurdly pretentious and would never supplant the real tree. We always gave it an honored place, but off to itself in the dining room. The real tree, in the living room, was ceiling-tall and covered with artificial diamonds, rubies, pearls, tinsel, snow, popcorn ropes, icicles, lights:

everything it could hold. Hank shopped lovingly and carefully each year for exactly the right tree. And it was always our one great surprise for the girls.

I hate the idea of having the tree all trimmed days before Christmas, or of children trimming it instead of their parents. I suppose those parents who do let children trim the tree, and who entertain or go out on Christmas Eve, are well within their rights. But I am impatient with such breaks in tradition, and can't understand, either, parents who distribute presents on Christmas Eve. I have heard some say they do this to get it over with. Get it over with! To me, the stealth and mystery of Christmas is a thrill I wouldn't share with anyone but Hank. And what is Christmas morning for, really, if not to share in the joy of children when they wake up and see that tree, and all their presents? How could anyone want to "get it over with"?

So we do it our way. All day before Christmas Eve, we are busy with our special, secret wrapping. The house is shiny, and the smudges on the wall are well-hidden by holly, ivy, and hemlock. We wait for Hank, who arrives with bulging packages, which he quickly hides. We eat anything that's handy for dinner; nobody is interested in food. And then we begin our Christmas Eve.

The fire in the fireplace is lighted, the children are dressed in their prettiest dresses, and we gather for the ceremony. First, we hang the stockings, put out something for Santa and his reindeer on a footstool, and Hank reads:

144

"And it came to pass in those days, that there went out a decree from Caesar Augustus. . . . And there were in the same country shepherds abiding in the field, keeping watch over their flock by night. . . ." From the King James or the Douay version; not from the new, improved Bible.

Jennie sings "Away in a Manger" and Miranda gives us "Jingle Bells." Louise does her specialty: "The Night Before Christmas," with but a little prompting from the book.

We all say "The Lord's Prayer" in French, and then it is time for the girls to put their presents for each other and for us in a special spot by the fireplace where Santa can find them and pile them in an impressive stack under the tree, after he trims it. Now the children are supposed to kiss everybody good night and go right to sleep. But tonight, something is different. Louise has disappeared and Jennie is announcing that they have a surprise and would like permission to stay up for a few minutes longer to present it.

Oh *no,* I thought. Not the dishwasher; not tonight. We always distribute gifts on Christmas morning. Besides, it can't be; it certainly isn't in the kitchen. Could it be hidden in a bedroom? No! It would have to be installed. Unless it's a portable? Anyway, I wish they had waited till morning.

I come back to the sound of Jennie's voice and try to follow. What is she saying? "——the honor to present: Miss Louise *Lamont!* In an extra, added, Christmas Eve attraction, as a particular surprise for her parents, but

145

especially Mommy, because it's her favorite: 'Cantique de Noel; Noel d'Adam.'"

And then Louise comes back, and bows. She smiles at us, and suddenly we hear a voice of infinite tenderness, purity, and beauty, singing:

> "Minuit, Chrétiens, c'est l'heure solenelle
> Ou l'homme Dieu descendit jusqu'a nous,
> Pour effacer la tache originelle
> Et de son père arreter le courroux."

Her face is lovelier far than any of the angels. God, forgive me, but isn't it? Her eyes, blazing with innocence and glory, are looking at a miracle.

> "Noel, Noel! voici le Redempteur!"

I don't think I can look, or listen, any more, but I can't move—the song is ended and there is silence.

I stumble to my feet and go into the bathroom and lock the door. Hank hastily goes to the kitchen and shuts the door.

I am not a sentimental woman, and this is not a sentimental story. It is supposed to be a comedy. So I will ask you not to join Hank in the kitchen, nor me in the bathroom. I ask, too, that you believe it was a full three weeks before I thought of a dishwasher again.

## 14

The bliss that had been Christmas remained with us for quite a while. Added to the fact that Hank, the girls, and I were more than usually loving, forbearing, and kind was that we got together in gay groups with Maria and her husband, with Jake, and others of our older, though not more valued, friends. Our house looked so festive and I was so happy that I looked almost as good as I felt I could look only in New York. This being the case, what else was there to do but have a party? We did, and it was as successful as we wanted it to be. I didn't know that Christmas could have such fringe benefits.

But alas—after the sparkle was stored away for another year, it became clear that the season's joy had disappeared with it. The potholders that the children had woven, lovingly and cunningly ("to help you do your housework!"), lost the magic they had when dressed in their holiday glitter and became just potholders.

On one especially irritating morning, when I had found it unusually difficult to convince Louise and Jennie of the value of dressing, breakfasting, and cleaning their faces and teeth in time to meet the bus, I'm ashamed to say that I fell into the error of declaiming to them on the gaiety of my unmarried life.

"Oh," I cried, "do you know what I used to do in the morning before I was married? I didn't have to leap out of bed and make breakfast and beg and plead with children to get dressed and eat! I didn't have to look for books, and mittens, and lunch tickets, and remind people old enough to have some sense of responsibility, over and over, about how late it was, and urge them to drink their milk! I *used* to get up whenever I felt like it! And have a quiet, peaceful breakfast, all by myself, and dress in the latest style, and brush my hair, and put on lipstick, and stroll leisurely to wherever my appointment was! I used to go outside, and the doorman would salute me, and smile, and say, very respectfully, 'Good morning, Miss Doyle. Would you be wanting a cab?' And I would smile and reply gently, 'No, thank you, James. It's such a beautiful day, I think I'll walk.' Then—" here I was getting carried away by the memory, and with eyes glazed, I walked to the window in the living room and stared outside "—then, I'd start up the street, and one day, when I was wearing a coat with a big, full skirt that swung back and forth as I walked, I passed a newsboy at Lexington and Forty-ninth Street, and when he saw me, he called out 'Dance balleriner dance!' and he smiled at me, and I smiled at him, and ever after, I always bought my New York *Times* from him. Then, I would stroll along to the office where I was going, and when I got to the building, the elevator starter would smile at me, and I would smile at him, and he would touch his cap, and he would say, 'Good morning, Miss Doyle——'"

"Never mind, Mommy," Miranda interrupted. "Don't think about those lonely days a long time ago when the olden days were here. Now you have us."

I stared at this small creature, so sure of herself, and then laughed out loud. So did Louise and Jennie. They wanted to hear more, but I didn't have time to go further into the long-lost career days past, for the bus had come and gone while I was regaling them with tales of high life, and I had to drive them to school.

After that lesson in blessing-counting, I began to devise ways of reminding myself of how lucky I was, in spite of the dailiness of life. I couldn't count on Miranda's always bringing me up short at times when I was tempted to pity myself.

For one thing, I started to accompany my chores with mood music, not the packaged variety, but albums especially designed by and for me. For the task of paying bills, I decided on *La Bohème* as the most appropriate accompaniment. While listening to Puccini's melodies, I could fool myself that I was crying over the plight of the poor Bohemians, instead of over the state of my bank account. As Rudolpho lamented the coldness of Mimi's little hand, I sobbed aloud over the cost of modern dentistry. As the poignant strains of "Musetta's Waltz" faded away, and Musetta shrieked at the pain caused by her tight shoes, her outcries drowned out mine, caused by the high price of little girls' shoes. While poor Mimi lay dying, I wiped away tears which I could almost convince myself were for her, but which were actually shed over the polite note on the next bill: "Has there been some misunderstanding?" "No, dear hardware store," I hummed. "No misunderstanding—no money." Usually I had the check-writing and the opera timed so that I was putting the last payment into its envelope and entering the balance in my ledger at the same time as Mimi succumbed to the ravages of tuberculosis. Thus, Rudolpho's cry of shocked dismay covered the sound of mine.

Probably the most therapeutic album of "music to be a housewife by" was one I put together on a day when my list of things to resent included certain shortcomings of my husband. I wondered how my life would be, had I married another. Starting the record player, I sat down and remembered men I used to know. The first record was of Duke Ellington and the Buck Clayton All-Stars. As I listened to Johnny Hodges' alto sax soloing in "I Got It Bad and That Ain't Good," I was dancing once more with Danny, darling Danny, at the St. Regis Roof. Later, while

Tommy Dorsey's orchestra filled the room with "Getting Sentimental Over You," I was sitting with Terrence, who was true-blue, sipping a cocktail at LaRue. True-blue Terrence was very rich, too. (Rich? He lived at Eighty-second Street and Park Avenue and his mother played the *harp*. You can't get any richer than that.) After a time, I believed I could hear again protestations of lasting devotion from Leo, the lion of courage, as I heard once more "our" song—"You'd Be So Nice to Come Home To." I thought, sitting there, of days when I used to feel it would have been nice to have Leo, the brave, the strong, the valiant, coming home to me. Then I heard "If They Asked Me, I Could Write a Book," and was holding hands at the movies once more with Bob, who was brilliant and bold.

When all the tunes were done, all the songs sung, I stood up, turned off the record player, and decided on sirloin steak for dinner. And later, when it was time to go and meet Hank at the station, I let the children get into the car and, "Wait a minute," I said. During the minute, I stood looking at the little statue (Hank's Christmas present to me) which stood beside the birdbath near the driveway. Hank had said: "Regard, Stephanie, my cabbage: St. Fiacre, an Irishman who came to France and there became the patron saint of tourists and gardeners!" Then I had bowed and said, "Vive la France!" And Hank had replied, "Erin Go Bragh—Up, the Rebels!"

I got into the car and, as we drove along, I began to sing, "Oh, it's so nice to be married; to be, be, be, be, really, really married. And a man, his wife, and family,

# WHATEVER YOU DO, DON'T PANIC

they should be happy as a bumblebee." The girls joined in on the chorus, and though we might not have had the words exactly right, might not have sung it as charmingly as Anna Held had for Florenz Ziegfeld, we must have put as much heart into it as did Anna.

My heart was in the song because Danny, the darling, was deeply deceitful. Thirty-three girls had he that he loved as well as me. And true-blue Terrence—he *was* true but to who(m)? To his mother, that's who. As for Leo, the lion, when he called me his lamb and earnestly swore his undying love, he was unwilling to wait for the day the Bible had in mind concerning the promise made to the lion and the lamb. And Bob, the brilliant and bold, was an early, a premature, beatnik: too proud to work for a living. It was I who paid at the movies, for his ticket and mine.

That's why, when I drew up to the station parking lot, I was glad to wait for the only male who mattered.

## 15

By February, that gladsome month, my personal life had become a mere breathing space between PTA tasks. I was asked to do this, and then to do that. Each committee chairman couched her request for help in terms that would have made refusal seem churlish—after all, they pointed out, the little tasks they dropped into my lap would take no more than fifteen minutes apiece. What they did not seem to realize was that there are only a certain number of fifteen minutes in each day.

The PTA had elected a new president—Mrs. Beige had

disappeared from the local scene, which was a great surprise to me since I had considered her a permanent institution. When I asked what had become of her, I learned that the entire Beige family had moved out of town; and the remarks that were uttered when Norma's name was mentioned would lead one to believe it was because they had something to live down. And all because someone in authority had been so indiscreet as to state publicly that Norma Beige was the best mother in town. Francesca said, "Well! If letting your children wear shoes two sizes too *small* is being a good mother!" Even Blanche—cloying-sweet, professionally kind Blanche— said, "If being a good mother is being *phlegmatic* and culturally *impoverished!*" Grazie baldly stated that Mrs. Beige had announced herself as being against water fluoridation. Although I had never been one of the lady's friends, I was saddened at the cruel words said behind her departed back. But what could I say? That perhaps she wasn't guilty? That they were convicting her on hearsay evidence?

The new power in the PTA made no difference to my career; the same series of fifteen-minute tasks continued to come my way.

"Look, Stephanie," Maria said to me one day, "if you would just get rid of some of that outside work, you might have an hour to spare for a nap each day."

"Oh, Maria," I replied, "a nap! If ever I had an hour to spare, I'd run away from home."

"Your trouble is that you don't leave any room to do the things you want to do. Can't you ever say 'no'?"

"Not to those committee chairmen," I confessed. "It would be like saying 'no' to General George Patton."

"Sometimes I want to give up on you," Maria said.

"Maria," I answered, "I have long since given up on myself."

Shortly after this occasion, I was summoned to a meeting of a committee presided over jointly by Francesca and Grazie. I got to Fran's house at the same time as a group of other mothers, some of whom I recognized. I had seen them only a few days before, during conference week at school.

Fran greeted me and the other mothers and led us into the library. We were seated around a low stone table as big as a mill wheel, which, closely inspected, revealed itself as having been a mill wheel. The boring in the center now contained a ceramic bowl holding a large-leaved philodendron that grew straight up and nearly touched the ceiling. It could have served as a room-divider, practically. Its size and position made it difficult for us to see each other across the table, but it *was* artistic and quaint.

While Fran was serving coffee, and cakes rich as Croesus, one of the guests noted that a certain Mrs. Jones was absent—again. She voiced the suspicion that Mrs. Jones, who was known to go to New York every Wednesday, must be in "deep analysis." A murmur of assent arose from around the mill wheel, but I kept my mouth shut. Wednesday, on our railroad, was Ladies' Day, when one could travel to the city at half-fare. And I remembered enough about New York to recall that it

155

was also matinee day. I knew that if I could afford it, I would go to New York every Wednesday myself—and not to lie around on a couch and tattle on my mother, either.

At this point Grazie arrived, greeting us with a smile that looked like a threat. Over the past several months, Grazie had been putting on weight, due, undoubtedly to the rich cake she had been eating at committee meetings. From looking like a frozen fish stick, she was now well on her way to resembling a loaf of Italian bread. When Grazie expressed regret at not having the meeting at her house, we all grew slightly uneasy—all except Fran, that is. She looked triumphant, and this look was enough to explain that once again she and Grazie had met in gladiatorial combat, and that Fran had carried off the prize: the honor of having the meeting at her house.

The meeting now began in earnest, with such topics as *My Fair Lady*, zoning laws, and gravel removal operations being discussed. After an hour or so, the session was declared closed. I was therefore caught off guard, the following morning, when Fran phoned to tell me to be sure that I was plentifully supplied with thumbtacks before I went to school.

"What thumbtacks?" I asked. "And what do you mean, before I go to school? I'm not going to the school. I found a list of names to call in my mailbox this morning, something about a dance in the gym next Saturday——"

"*Honey!*" Fran interrupted. "You were at the meeting yesterday. Don't you remember being assigned to the team in charge of decorating the gym? For heaven's sake! Forget those calls! That's the work of some other team. You're on *mine!*"

I refrained from pointing out that no one at the meeting had so much as mentioned decorations, the gym, the Saturday dance, or thumbtacks. I contented myself with knowing that at last I had some idea what the meeting had been about, as Fran hung up with a few more words of encouragement. "Come on, Miranda," I said, after I found a couple of boxes of thumbtacks in Hank's cache of hardware. "We're going to school again."

In the gym, we found hundreds of pictures (the work of pupils) obviously needing to be tacked up on the walls. Otherwise, except for Miranda and me, the gym was empty. We waited a while for the rest of the thumbtack team to get there, but nobody did. "Miranda," I said, "it looks like the other helpers are going to be late. How would you like to get off the bench and into the game?"

Our first task was to stack the pictures, which had been painted on heavy paper, in relation to the classes that had produced them—Kindergarten, First, Second Grade, and so on. Then, assisted by Miranda, whose chief contribution was criticizing the various works of art, I climbed up and down a ladder for a couple of hours, shoving thumbtacks. As noon approached, Miranda let it be known that she was becoming less interested in art than in the idea of food. I took her to the cafeteria, waited for Jennie, handed her over to her sister, and commanded Jennie to see that Miranda was fed and afterwards returned to me in the gym. I was hungry myself, and would have welcomed a cup of coffee, but in my condition I was unable to bring myself to remain in the midst of that milling crowd.

I returned to my job and was hanging the last of the pictures when the door of the gym opened and Fran walked in. She swept the walls with a glance. "That one is crooked," she said.

Slowly I descended the ladder. Slowly I took a deep breath. "*Thanks*, Madame Chairman," I said. "Thank you enormously." My voice returned from the corners of the gym and it was not until then that I realized it was the loudest voice I had. "I could hardly wait for you to get here and point out my mistake. Your *team*—that's me, I'm *it*—your team had a hard time without your being on hand with advice! *Now listen, you!* If you want your dinner, DON'T INSULT THE COOK!"

And then I became deeply ashamed. Already Francesca had the upper hand, if only she knew it. "But my *dear!*" she cried. "Please forgive me. I had no *idea* that you were working alone. The truth is that you are the only dependable member of my team. Let's have a cigarette."

We lit our cigarettes, and Fran went on. "You don't know what I've been through this past week! My son Clyde—you know Clyde. You know the sort of boy he is: his capabilities, his potential——"

The deepest misery was in her voice. More than ever, I was ashamed. "What about Clyde?" I asked. "What's happened?"

Fran's face drowned in sorrow and I waited for some ghastly piece of news. "We've been locked in a contest of wills," she said. "I naturally refused to enter into open conflict—to *admit* the rupture—for the past week I simply haven't been speaking to him."

Her face began to go under for the third time, but she continued. "And do you know what has happened?" Fran asked. "Do you know what he has been doing for spite? He refuses to spend his hour listening to good music. He insists on turning his back on Schönberg. And not only that! This morning I caught him putting his breakfast prunes in his pocket. As a result, the laundress quit. I tried to make her understand that Clyde's animosity was directed in a perfectly normal, healthy channel—towards me, his mother—but the woman wouldn't listen to reason. She said she didn't care whom he was mad at, she wasn't going to wash any more prunes. I guess this wasn't the first time Clyde put his prunes in his pockets."

"How do things stand now?" I asked carefully, after a long sigh and a short silence from Fran.

"I demanded a showdown," Fran answered. "I ordered Clyde to choose his punishment. He said he didn't care what the punishment was, as long as it wasn't Schönberg, but I had no intention of letting him get away with that!"

"What did you do?"

"I told the cook to fix a special treat for dessert tonight —chocolate soufflé—and I made it clear to that young man that he wasn't going to get any."

"That's telling him," I said.

Our conversation was interrupted by the entrance of Grazie, who took one look at the walls of the gym and screamed. I jumped, and saw that Fran had jumped, too.

"*Francesca!*" Grazie demanded. "May I ask what your imbecilic team has done? My team took all these pictures *down* from the walls, day before yesterday. *Your* team was supposed to return them to the art department and get a new batch. Are we to have the same pictures hanging on these walls FOREVER?"

The two chairmen began to exchange compliments, and I took advantage of their preoccupation to effect a quiet, even a sneaky, retreat. Hastening to the cafeteria, I rescued Miranda and we went home. We stopped to see if there was any real mail, but the box was empty.

"Maybe the mailman didn't come today," said Miranda.

"No, that's impossible, Miranda," I said. "He has to come, every day."

"Even when it's his mother's birthday?"

"Even when it's his own birthday."

After this Miranda was silent, until we reached the kitchen door. Then, as I was opening it, she said: "Well, I guess that's right. If you have a job to do, you have to do it."

After I put her to bed for her nap, I looked hard at me and the PTA, and thought about Miranda's observation about the mailman. "If you have a job to do, you have to do it." And my job was being a housewife.

I picked up the list of names I was supposed to call, and wished once more that my name was followed by an "ecp," as were a few on the list. My assumption had been that "ecp" meant "especially conscientious people"—until I was told that it was a kind of "do not disturb" sign for people "engaged in creative pursuits." In this community

—where there was never even standing room at any meeting to discuss the "gifted" child—sculptors, painters, artists, writers, actors, and such were more than respected. They were revered.

"Wish they considered gardening a creative pursuit," I thought. "If I was an 'ecp,' they wouldn't always be after me—wait a minute! How am I going to get time for the garden when spring comes if I don't start saying 'no' to these chairmen——"

At that moment the phone rang, and I tried not to hear it, because I knew it was going to be a call from the chairman who had left that list of names. Unfortunately, I am unable to let a phone ring. I tried it once, and to this day I am still obsessed (when I think of it) by what I might have missed. So after the phone had blasted the quiet a few more times, I picked it up.

The caller was Francesca. "Sweetie!" she exclaimed. "You know that list you mentioned this morning? Well that, Honey, was the list of people you were supposed to call to help you hang the *right* pictures this morning! Grazie told me she left it—she must have forgotten to write a note saying what it was for."

I was speechless, but Fran was not. She must have forgotten that it was possible for me to lose my temper, because she went on: "So I was thinking, if you call a few of those people right now, you can get them to come on over to the gym with you and remedy your mistake. How soon do you think you can make it?"

Closing my eyes, I thought hard about my garden, holding the thought like a talisman. Then I answered

162

Fran, and what I had to say was so easy that I was astonished I hadn't been able to say it before.

"Fran, I'm sorry. I can't go back to the gym. As a matter of fact, I was just going to call you and tell you that I have to resign. Yes, from your committee, and from every other committee there is. Right now."

And resign I did. I called all the chairmen and told them they had a vacancy to fill. I made no excuses. All I said was that I couldn't keep up with so many outside tasks and my family at the same time. When I had made the last call, I hung up and went to the bedroom. Settling down on the bed with Miranda, I took a nap.

16

After much backing and filling, much coyness, much coquetry, spring returned. She spent all of March and part of April coming to town for a day or two, smiling and winking, and flying away again. But at last, early in April, she quit fooling around and settled down for her allotted time.

I checked and rechecked my gardening encyclopedia and decided that I could begin planting with no fear of losing anything to the frost. I was frantic to begin—my head throbbed with visions of what a patch of color could be made of the shaded area that paralleled the driveway, filled with begonias, impatiens, sweet williams, violets, pansies, cathedral bells, and columbines. Right opposite the big dining-room window there was a sunny spot where sat my statue of St. Fiacre, a birdbath, and a feeder. These were waiting for spring bulbs to flower, along with myrtle; and afterwards, a succession of lilies, zinnias, and marigolds, and lastly, asters and chrysanthemums.

One Sunday evening I was sitting entranced by color photos of rose gardens in one of my many catalogues, wondering why anyone found Gertrude Stein obtuse. "A rose *is* a rose is a rose is a rose." Of course it is. As I was mentally agreeing with Miss Stein, Hank said, "Stephanie, can you get a sitter for Friday? I know where I can get tickets for *The Music Man*."

It took me quite some time to get my mind off the roses and on to what Hank was saying and then, "Oh, Hank!" I answered. "Didn't you see the New York *Times* today?"

Hank looked baffled, but interested. Experience had taught him that though it took some doing, he could eventually make sense out of my remarks.

"What has the New York *Times* got to say that would prevent your going to see *The Music Man*?" he asked. "Is there a bomb scare planned for Friday?"

Despite his obtuseness, I remained patient as I explained: "I mean 'Things To Do This Week.' In the *garden* section," I went on, as he continued to look blank. "My goodness, there's not a moment to lose—here, I'll read it, so you'll see what I have to do—not counting 'If There Is Time'!"

WHATEVER YOU DO, DON'T PANIC

"Never mind," he said. "I'm a hydrangea here, myself."

The next morning, after seeing Louise and Jennie off on the school bus, Miranda and I took Hank to the station. While driving away from there, and on to other errands, I reflected on how silly it had been of me to think, as I did before I could drive, that five out of ten drivers were out to kill me. Seven out of ten was more like it. My driving habits were, for Catatonia, eccentric. I irritated a lot of fellow motorists; I drove too close to the car behind me, stopped at stop signs, observed the posted speed limits, and waited for red lights to turn green. The other drivers' attitude towards me made me feel unloving towards them and candor compels me to admit that there were times when we exchanged intemperate words. Much of my worry time at night was devoted to fretting over the chances of meeting one or more of these antagonists at a party. But although it wasn't all chitlings and corn pone, driving was a freedom and a privilege I wouldn't be without. It had resulted in more benefits than I had foreseen. Even going to the supermarket wasn't the "adventure" it used to be. I didn't have to go on Saturdays; I could choose a day when the store wasn't so crowded. For instance, on Monday mornings even the ladybutcher wasn't so forbidding.

Miranda and I made short work of laying in supplies at the supermarket and continued to my favorite store, a minute shop of the sort that used to be known as a "general store." It was called Ricardo's Fruit and Vegetable Stand, but the business, despite the size of the store, had expanded to include almost everything. It was owned and run by one big family, consisting of great, grand, and plain parents, and innumerable children. Ricardo's never seemed to close and I never went there without finding the whole family there, glad to be there and pleased to greet a customer. Besides the joy of doing business with people who liked their work, there was the lagniappe that Ricardo made every woman who came into his shop feel that she was the most beautiful, admirable, and intelligent female this side of the Rocky Mountains, the one woman he most wanted to see. Needless to say, he did a thriving business.

We went into the store, and Miranda started to inspect the stock. She asked Ricardo: "Are these living gloves so flexible that you can pick up a thin dime with them?" Ricardo assured her of this remarkable fact and added, "I promise you, Miss Lamont, that if you fail to be entirely satisfied, I will cheerfully refund the purchase price." Miranda gravely nodded her satisfaction, but chose a coloring book instead. I got what I wanted—several glowing azaleas and some of Ricardo's flattery—and we left.

Going to Front Street, we went into the Spice of Life Variety Store, where I was glad to see that Alice, the young clerk, had taken steps to improve her appearance and her attitude. (Oh, don't look for her on the boardwalk at Atlantic City, for you'll never find her competing for Miss Anything, but at least she has become more human.)

"Hello, Alice," I said. "How's your mother?" She almost answered, did nod, and even, to Miranda's pleasure, scribbled her fingers through my daughter's hair.

I took a look at the sock bins and said: "Listen, Alice, how about some size-seven socks?"

Bemusedly, Alice looked at all the bins. Then, with an effort, she returned her gaze to me. "Fresh out, I guess," she said.

"You know, when I used to try for size sixes, there were no size sixes. There was always, invariably, everything *but* sixes. Now that I want sevens, there are thousands of everything but sevens."

"How about that?"

I turned to leave and—accolade of accolades!—Alice said, "Want me to take a look inna stockroom?"

"Oh, Alice!" I said, when I had recovered from the shock, "thank you, but no. I can't wait."

It was true that I couldn't wait. I remembered that on one occasion, Alice had been ordered to go and look for something for me in the stockroom. She was gone an unconscionable time; had forgotten what she had been sent for, even that she had been sent. When at last she ambled back into the front of the store, she had approached me and said, "May I help you?"

Sockless, but not unhappy, Miranda and I started back home, eager to get on with our gardening. As I drove, I thought of how the town had grown since we had moved there.

As we turned the corner and approached our house, I saw that both sides of our road were lined with Cadillacs. "Laborers," I decided, automatically, since they were the only people in Catatonia who drove Cadillacs. "Some road repair, or building project." While we were putting the groceries away and then getting out the gardening tools, I reflected on the days when ten or twelve workingmen used to arrive in one pickup truck, now each man had his own Cadillac to take him to the job. And then it hit me. I jumped up and ran outside with Miranda following close behind. Standing in the driveway, I stared, as all the laborers converged on a spot under my nose, and began shouting to each other. I approached them and asked what their plans were, and their boss announced, laconically, that they were going to build a house—right on the very edge of the two-acre lot beside our house. Whoever lived in the new house would be able to see every move we made, since the one big window in our place would be in a direct line from the new house.

I turned and went back into the house. Miranda followed shortly, and asked why I wasn't going to start the planting. I explained that I had just remembered something important I had to take care of inside. Then she asked permission to watch the fascinating operation next door; I said, "Yes, but stay on the terrace." I poured myself a cup of coffee, lit a cigarette, and sank down on the kitchen floor. I sat there for a while and then called Hank to say that I'd love to see *The Music Man*.

During the ensuing weeks, which were made horrid by blasting, bulldozers, and bellowing workmen, I stayed away from home as much as possible. More than ever, I resented our house, which rendered all things ridiculous.

One morning we woke to find that the Cadillacs, carpenters, and assorted earth-movers had left. Shortly thereafter, a van arrived next door, depositing, among other things, an outdoor barbecue, blatantly new and the size of an open-hearth furnace in a steel mill. The outdoor-lover's requisite was put on the terrace of the new house and I shuddered at what it indicated for summer Saturday nights. All those "cookouts," much amusing of many palates with beer, and endless "For He's a Jolly Good Fellow's" far into the dawn of Sunday mornings.

I knew that I would have to learn to keep my own voice down; these neighbors would be so close that they could hear my cakes fall, let alone the merry bawling in which I conversed with our daughters. Moving away from the dining-room window, I walked up to the living room—thinking of all the window shades I would have to buy, wishing we could afford a fence.

Days passed. I was aware that a family had moved in next door, but I tried to remain unconscious of them. The only thing that cheered me during that time was a phone call from Rosemary Donovan in Chinnuppe, Connecticut. She invited all of us for a weekend visit. We hadn't seen Rosemary and her husband Tom in their new house; we corresponded and had met them briefly in New York the once or twice I had been able to go there. Hank and I and the children were eager for the weekend; the Donovans—like the Canwells—were more than friends.

Late on Friday afternoon, the day before we planned to go to Chinnuppe, I was in the dining room with the girls, helping them decide what to take on the trip. Glancing out the window, I noticed a girl on the terrace next door, surrounded, like a mother partridge, by several small children. When I remarked that their mother should have chosen an older sitter to take care of so many, such little, children, "But Mommy," said Jennie, "that's not a sitter! That's their mother; that's Mrs. Bennington."

"Don't be childish," I said. "Why, that girl's no more than fourteen."

"She is too the mother, Mommy," said Louise. "We went over to see her and met the children. She likes us. She said we were lovely girls."

Cap and bells again, I thought. My *children* have called on the new neighbors. I should have—never mind all my excuses about not wanting to "intrude." Looking at the girl, thinking that she had said of our children, "lovely girls," seeing how vulnerably young she seemed, I promised myself that I would call on her. No need to get involved; just be nice, for heaven's sake! Maybe Monday, I thought. Right now I have all this packing to do.

The girls and I were soon absorbed again in our task, and when an hour or so had passed, I looked out the window again and was alarmed to see, leaving the new house, the Mother Shipton salesman. "Come on!" I said to myself. "Don't wait until tomorrow. Call on that girl right now." I grabbed two of my choicest begonias, and hastened over. The girls followed close behind.

When Mrs. Bennington answered my ring, I introduced myself reservedly, and offered the plants. Immediately, we were engulfed by children; like escaped mercury, they were hard to track, but I concluded that there were at least five boys and girls. Like our children, they hugged, chortled, cooed, shrieked their delight at seeing us. Mrs. Bennington also appeared glad to see us. She served milk and cookies in the kitchen to all the children, and asked me to sit out on the terrace. As we went out there, she grinned and said, "If you can make it around this monster!" nodding at the grill. "The children's idea of living in the country is eating hamburgers outside. Don and I are trying to make them appreciate the benefits of a dining room." Feeling guilty, I sat down and told myself that I was in great danger of breaking a leg if I didn't stop leaping to conclusions.

Mrs. Bennington offered me a cup of coffee, but I declined, saying that I didn't have time—I had to go to the station for Hank. At this, her smile faded a bit, but she thanked me for the plants. "I'm not sure I can take care of them, though," she said. "I don't know much about flowers."

I suppressed the temptation to initiate a discussion on gardening, and after a few minutes became brave enough to broach the subject of Mother Shipton. "I can see how you might feel it's none of my business," I said, "and it isn't. But I saw that truck and that man, and thought how grateful I would have been for a warning about how those people operate . . ."

"Oh, thank you, Mrs. Lamont," she answered. "I do appreciate it. And you're so right. When I called the Better Business Bureau to check up on them, they said just what you said!"

"Huh!" I thought. "Who's protecting whom? This little lady is not so defenseless as she looks."

"Fine," I said aloud, and feeling briskly inefficient, rose to depart. As I entered the kitchen, where the children were gayly spilling milk and crunching cookies underfoot, I noticed that at least one of Mrs. Bennington's little ones seemed to be peeking over the top of a mushroom.

Then I looked at the mother again, and said formally that I hoped she'd be happy in her new home. She said, "I'm sure I will be—when I get used to country living. The nights are awfully quiet, aren't they?"

I agreed, and noticed again how very young she looked. With an ache, partly for my own sake, I thought of how living here was bound to age her. I knew perfectly well that if we hadn't moved to Catatonia, I wouldn't have a single gray hair, in spite of my more than thirty years. After all, I had lived my whole life without any, before moving to the country, and now I was beginning to look like a herring gull.

Maybe, I thought, maybe Mrs. Bennington is wise enough to check with the Better Business Bureau. And maybe she is a step ahead of where you were when you moved here, in other ways. For one thing, she can drive. But I thought of all the other things that this woman would have to face, and learn to live with. Looking at the clock, I remarked, "You know, it's not so late as I thought. I'd like to change my mind about that coffee, if you don't mind, Mrs. Bennington."

"Please," she said, smiling, "call me Anne, won't you? That's my name. What's yours?"

## 17

Our trip to Chinnuppe was a typical American-family outing—fraught with more drama, more impact, and more emotional power than the most hair-raising thriller. Before we started, Hank assembled us outside, and during the ensuing scene I was tempted more than once to call out, "Hey, Colonel, get those men out of the hot sun!" General Montgomery at El Alamein couldn't have been more explicit in his directions than Hank, detailing what he expected of the children during the trip.

"I presume," said he (among many, many other things),

174

"that you have all gone to the bathroom. Very well. Now: you may converse quietly, but you may not shout or fight. You may play games, like 'I see something green,' but you may *not* argue about who wins! You may compete in counting out-of-state license plates, IF YOU CAN DO SO WITHOUT QUARRELING. And most important of all, under no circumstances, at any time, whatsoever, for any reason at all, is anybody, *anybody*, to ask 'HOW MANY MORE MILES.' Have I made myself perfectly clear?" We all agreed that he had—yes, indeed—he permitted us to get into the car, and we got underway. We drove for a while in what was a rather nervous silence. Then:

Louise: What do you think they'll have to eat? I hope not oysters.

Me: No matter what they serve, you'll eat it, all of you, and no remarks, hear?

Miranda: Even asparagus?

Me: Even asparagus. Listen, asparagus is good for you. Besides, it *tastes* good, after you get used to it.

Jennie: I don't want to get used to it.

Louise: Neither do I.

Miranda: Neither do I.

Me: Negative, negative! You can at least try! If you begin by eating a little, and then eat a little more the next time it's served, you'll get to love it. It's like this: when I first saw pink and orange combined, I couldn't stand it, but now my eyes are used to it—trained, you might say. You train your taste buds the same way, see?

Miranda: I still don't like it.

Me: Never mind! Eat it anyway; it's good for you.

Jennie: I don't care if it is good for me. I still don't like pink and orange.

Louise: Me either.

Miranda: I agree. I agree.

Me: Oh, so now you all know better than Matisse!

Hank (entering the conversation): Oh, my God!

Me (anxiously): What's the matter? Did you forget your wallet?

Hank (in a loud, uncalled-for tone): No! Will you please be quiet?

I couldn't think why he was so cross, since he had specifically said we might converse quietly. Maybe he was a little nervous. Anyway, we all stopped talking until we got on the Merritt Parkway, where we fast approached an apparently deranged balloon man who was hawking his bright, buoyant wares on the shoulder of the road where everybody speeded by at well over fifty miles an hour. Quickly, Hank and I tried to interest the girls in the beauties of a dying elm—a tree that was directly opposite the balloon man. Our exclamations and exhortations to "Look, look! See the lovely tree" fell upon a stony silence. After nineteen minutes of this menacing quietude, Miranda said, icily: "I don't think it's very nice of you to buy a poor girl no balloon." The other two agreed at the top of their lungs. It was difficult for Hank and me to out-holler them, but at last we succeeded. The ensuing tension was so highly charged that I was glad when Jennie spoke.

"Daddy," she said.

Hank didn't answer.

"Daddy, AREN'T YOU GOING TO ANSWER ME?" Jennie shouted.

Seeing that Hank was determined not to hear, I replied, "Your father forgot to tell you you're not supposed to speak to the driver, Jennie."

Jennie: Mommy.

Me: Yes, Honey; what is it?

Jennie: About how many more hours before we get there?

Hank (almost strangling): I TOLD YOU NOT TO ASK! I INSISTED THAT ABOVE ALL ELSE, YOU NOT ASK THAT!

Jennie: You said not to ask how many more *miles*, not how many more hours! All I want to know——

Hank: That's ENOUGH!

The girls subsided into mutinous mutterings, which gradually trickled away. Time passed, and when we deserted the Parkway to stop for milkshakes in a small Connecticut town, harmony was restored. After we were on our way again and while we were waiting for a light to change, we noticed a young man leaning against the side of a building in the town where we had had our snack. The youth had a beard, so, of course, one of us said: "Beaver!" When the light turned to green, Hank shot the car forward, shouting, "Ste—PHA—N I E!" and I take an oath—I honest-to-goodness swear—it wasn't until I heard Hank's outcry that I realized it was I who had made the blunder.

Unable to find our way back to the Parkway, we had to drive through the next town. On its outskirts we passed a graveyard, and in the car mirror, Hank noticed that the girls had blown up their cheeks with air and were pointing their thumbs upward.

"WHAT ARE YOU DOING NOW?"

Patiently, the girls explained that when you pass a graveyard, you must point your thumbs up and blow hard—that by this rite, you insured your being blown up, not down, when you die. Before Hank could say "Ste—PHA—N I E!", I rushed to my defense. "I didn't tell them that! Honestly! I never even *heard* of such a thing! They must have picked it up from the Brownies!"

That was the last of the major crises attendant upon the journey; the small ones, I'll pass over. Soon thereafter, we arrived in Chinnuppe and were warmly greeted by our friends.

The next morning, as Rosemary and I were having coffee, I asked where our men and our children were.

"They were all up very early," answered Rosemary. "The children have all gone on a truffle hunt, they said, in the woods. Tom and Hank have gone for the Sunday papers."

We sat and chatted; I told Rosemary once more how much I liked her house. It was much like that of the Canwells, but larger. I told Rosemary more about Maria, and thought again how very like these two friends of mine were; probably the most capable, intelligent, and kindest women I had ever known.

When Hank and Tom eventually returned, I was interested to see that Hank had a dreamy—not to say dazed—look and that Tom seemed mysteriously pleased. "Mama," Hank began, and it came out a bit weakly. "Mama, come for a ride. I want to show you something."

I saw that Rosemary and Tom were exchanging glances. "Go ahead," urged Rosemary. "I know what he wants to show you—I want you to see it, too."

Hank and I left, but he would say nothing to relieve my curiosity. After about ten minutes, he stopped the car and we got out. He led me up a winding driveway, and as we walked between old, graceful hemlocks, in silence, I confess that I thought he (and the Donovans) had gone mad. Then, as we reached the end of the drive, I beheld a house that I knew instantly had been built for us, some time late in the eighteenth century.

"Innisfree," I heard myself saying, "Innisfree—good morning."

How can I tell about that house? Hank and I walked slowly through its square, beautifully proportioned rooms, nearly all of which had a fireplace. In the kitchen, the fireplace was so high you could step into it. I can't describe the appeal, the charm, the sheer rightness of the house and its grounds. Like our house in Catatonia, it stood high on a hill, but there all similarity ended. This house had a view of Long Island Sound; it had privacy, insured by old pines and hemlocks; it had been loved and

179

cherished. And on the south side, there was a thing I had never expected to see: a walled garden.

After we had explored the house and its grounds, Hank said, "Stephanie, how would you like to live here?"

I looked at him reproachfully. Seeing my expression, he hastened to say that Tom had showed him the house in the hope that we would want it. I couldn't believe it when Hank assured me that the house was within our means. He explained that the Donovans had talked to the owner, who was anxious to sell for only one thousand dollars more than we had paid for our place in Catatonia. When I heard that three and one-half acres went with the house—that Chinnuppe's zoning regulations provided that no house could have less than three acres—I was practically stunned.

When we got back to the Donovans' and had talked off our excitement, Rosemary clarified my confusion. "Remember the stores in New York that advertised, 'a little off the Avenue; a lot off the price?' That's the principle, Steffie! Chinnuppe is too far for most commuters, but all of them living here think the extra train ride is worth it."

We left to go back to Catatonia late that afternoon, with the understanding that I would return alone on the following Tuesday. At that time, I would talk over terms with the owner of what was already "Innisfree" in my mind, and would be, always. Hank and I said nothing to the children about the house. We knew the many details we would have to take care of before we could move. But I knew in my blood and in my bones that "Innisfree" would be ours, that we would be living in it before the year was out. When at length we arrived in the driveway of our house in Catatonia, and the girls chorused "Home again!" I silently said, "No, not home. I know where home is, yours and mine, and you will, too, soon enough."

## 18

I spent all of Monday in a trance, coming out of it just
long enough to make practical plans for an early getaway
on Tuesday morning. It was Spring Vacation Week for
the girls; all the schools were closed and it was no problem
to arrange for Gladys to stay with the children while I
went back to buy our house.

As soon as Gladys had taken all the children for a walk
in the woods on Tuesday morning, and I was alone, I
began dressing for my trip. Needing a towel, I opened the
linen closet to get one, and grinned again at the message

I LOVE HORSES.
I WISH WHISH I
HAD a HORSE.
I LOVE
mY
MOMMY
SINCERELY
LOUISE
LAMONT

john huehnergarth

Louise had written neatly on the inside of the door, when she had begun to learn to write: "I love horses. I whish I had a horse. I love my mommy. Sincerely, Louise Lamont." The first time I saw this cryptic note, I had lunged into her room and shouted to my eldest: "Louise! Just look what you've done to that door. Surely you're old enough to know better! Go and fix it at once!" She had leaped up and hastened to obey. When I had checked on the cleaning up, I discovered that she had drawn a line through the "whish" and had substituted "wish."

Thinking of selling the house, I wondered, "What am I going to do about this. Well, it's one more problem, that's all. Hank will have to buy a new door for the linen closet, and we'll take this one off and take it with us." With my mind on the subject of doors, I had a sudden inspiration—why had I never thought of it before! Whoever bought this house could put one of those attractive louvered doors into the opening of the living room that led to the bathroom. "That will shut off the view of the bathroom!" I said to myself. "It won't matter that nobody ever remembers to shut the bathroom door. Besides, the shutters will make the living room look more spacious, more square, and the fireplace will seem to be centered——" Slowly, I walked from room to room, saying to the house: "You do see, don't you, that we can't go on like this? It's no good, I tell you; a house like you, a family like us. It's not your fault; it's nobody's fault. I've tried, God knows I've tried, but it's no good, I tell you."

I was sorry for having kicked the house that time (all

right, those times) and glad to know that whoever bought it would be able to spend more time and money to make it attractive than we had been in a position to do. "After all," I thought, "the new people won't have to buy a roof, expel termites, buy a new oil burner, and paint, and put in another bathroom and all those bedrooms!"

When I had dressed and was about to get into the car, I saw that a single, lonely daffodil was blooming in front of the statue of St. Fiacre. I turned and glared at the house and said: "There! You see? Things can *never* be right between you and me! Those daffodils weren't supposed to bloom until the myrtle does! *Good-bye!*"

I drove off and as I approached the entrance to the Parkway, I thought that if it wasn't for Maria, I wouldn't be able to go by myself to see about the house. I shook off the unpleasant feeling I had at moving away from a friend once more. Thinking of all the friends from whom I had been cut loose, I determined that this would not happen with Maria and her family. "Chinnuppe is not so far away," I told myself. Then I began to plan a party to which I could invite the new girl next door: "Maria and Ed will like her and her husband. And it will be good for Anne to know Maria. No reason for her to wait as long as I did before finding a friend in Catatonia."

Driving along, I thought that there were not many people in Catatonia whom I would miss—not many people and not many things. Then, "They don't have a beach in Chinnuppe," I said. "Goody!" I answered. "The children and Hank will miss the beach," I went on. "Well, they'll just have to learn as I have that there's more to life than swimming," I decided. Contemplating the walled garden I was going to have, I found myself wondering if I would enjoy it as much as the one I had begun myself. "Bet your life I will!" I shouted.

I concentrated on anticipations of the gracious life we would live in the new house. "I can be a lady there," I thought. "I can wear floppy straw hats, and voile and chiffon dresses in the garden, and no one—in the PTA or any other organization—will dream of imposing on a lady who is the mistress of such a house. I'll get up early every morning, and we will have a *schedule*. The girls will be so easy to care for, in such a relaxed atmosphere. No more daydreaming in the kitchen for me—I'll do all the chores as soon as I get up, and then I'll embroider, or paint, or do needlepoint for an hour. Then, lunch, and I'll rest for an hour, and in the afternoon, I'll have other ladies in for tea, and nobody will show up in Bermuda shorts. We'll have formal dinners with linen napkins and the family will gather afterwards for poetry readings in the evenings. So soothing! The girls will all go to sleep quietly then. And we won't always be on top of each other, the way we are in our little house." I thought, then, that even if we lived in Blenheim Castle the girls would never be found more than six feet away from me. I used to think that they suspected I would forget I had them if they were out of my pocket, so to speak, for more than a minute. Further research into the subject had changed my views. I concluded that they remained within the sight and sound of me in order to be sure they understood clearly what commands they planned to ignore. How dreadful, for instance, if instead of not cleaning their teeth, they failed to hang up their nightgowns.

But the larger house would be easier to live in for other reasons. We could be together with more space. And then later, when the girls were older and we allowed them to start having dates (say around twenty-five, twenty-six years) it would be convenient to have rooms to which Hank and I could retire. Thus dreaming, planning, enjoying our glorious future, I was surprised to discover that the journey had ended. I was there, at the Donovans' house, where I was going to meet the owner of our Innisfree.

I parked the car in the driveway and walked up the kitchen steps. When my tapping wasn't answered, I walked into the kitchen, calling, "Hello" just as Rosemary, looking distressed, hung up the phone. "Oh, Stephanie," she said, "I didn't hear your car—sit down." I couldn't. Seeing Rosemary Donovan flustered made me too uneasy. It was as though the sun had become erratic. When she said, "Stephanie, believe me, I don't know how to tell you this," I grew faint with terror.

Sure that she had received word of a tragedy involving Hank or the children, I was nearly relieved to hear the heartbreaking information she did have. The relief was momentary—like when I stubbed a toe; I knew it was going to hurt a lot more in just a minute. "How am I going to break the news to Hank!" I thought. "He will be so disappointed, too!"

For the news that Rosemary tried to tell me, gently, was that the owner of our dream house—my own hallucination hall—had told her that the price quoted included only one-eighth of an acre; that the rest of the land was going to be cut up into building lots of a similar size. For just a moment, I forgot my own disappointment in agony at the desecration. Innisfree—shorn of its pines, its hemlocks, and its garden; Innisfree, naked and surrounded by brazen little all-alike houses. Fortunately, the doorbell rang just as Rosemary finished the tale. Tearing her hair, she said, "Do sit down, Stephanie! I'll get rid of whoever it is, *this* time, as soon as I can."

I sat down and tried not to care. That was all I wanted; not to care. In a moment, I became conscious of a voice in the living room; a voice that seemed to have come from another place, another time. I said, "I have been here before." Then I said, "No, that's not right. This is where I came in." And I bowed my head and no longer tried not to care, not to cry. Not because the voice I heard was saying, at first, "Good morning comma I hope it is not too early to call period The fact is comma I was on my way to the school——"

My tears flowed because, out of the wealth of precise articulation, there soon fell upon my ears the words "double sessions." That was the bell that tolled for me. That put pennies on the eyes of my dead hopes.

Rosemary returned in exactly ten and one-fifth seconds for Mrs. Beige's tea-with-cream-please-if-there-is-any-handy. I didn't want to add to her bother, but couldn't help asking: "Why double sessions? I thought the citizens of Chinnuppe were more than prosperous."

Frantically, Rosemary whispered, "They are! Prosperous

and cheap! They voted down the new school. Now they say if we don't like double sessions, we can send our children to private schools! Excuse me, Stephanie, I'll be back as soon as she leaves."

In the fullness of Mrs. Beige's time, Rosemary returned and, "Honey, please don't change your mind about moving up here," she said. "We're forming committees right now to insure a majority vote when the school building issue comes up again. And we're going to fight to prevent that woman from chopping up all that land! Why, the zoning laws—she can't get away with it! I'll start calling people right away and we'll hire a lawyer——"

"Oh, Rosemary," I interrupted. "What's the use? So you do get the law to uphold the zoning." (I didn't have the courage to tell her how remote were her chances.) "Then the woman will ask thousands more for the house, much more than we could afford."

None too soon, we said good-bye, and I found myself back in the car, saying, "Don't you ever dare to go there, don't you ever dare to find. Lovely things like that is almost always in your mind." Not that we wouldn't go back to see the Donovans. Of course we would. But we would give "Innisfree" as wide a berth, I knew, as we did our old apartment in the Fifties, whenever we were in New York.

Unhappy as I had ever been, I began to have an inkling of how rootless, lost, and longing displaced persons must feel. Then, hearing the wheels start to move in my head, I warned my brain, "Look out. Here comes A Thought. Displaced persons—that's it. That's what we are; all of us commuter families. Not pioneers; nothing so grand as frontiersmen carving out of a wilderness a new empire, with covered wagons, muskets, and the strength of our arms. We are only DP's, unwelcome but tolerated because of our relative affluence. Even in New York (this I hated to admit) we are sneered at by some as those who use the metropolis merely as an office, and in the suburbs we are condemned as those who regard the towns and villages as just so many bedrooms. No wonder that we're all running scared; no wonder that we all seem unnatural, being constantly on the defensive as we are." I reflected further, and saw us all as exaggerated people; so much more, so irritatingly more like ourselves than we would be where we had roots, families before us, to prove who we are. So. That's it. "No villains?" I asked. "No villains. Francesca is so much sillier, Blanche is so much sweeter, Grazie is so much crueler, and I am so much more scared and ineffectual than we would have been had we stayed at home in Oklahoma, Ohio, or Little Neck. Only Maria is herself. She's one of the few who would be themselves anyplace. And our children, all our children, too—they don't have to prove who they are. Maria, and the children. As for the rest of us, we'll just have to fight it out along these (clearly defined) lines if it takes all our lives. Because we can't go home again. We have to make our homes wherever we find ourselves."

Irked by the necessity of seeking the comforts of philosophy, I began to grouse about the prospect of continued association with the likes of Fran, Blanche, Grazie, and their kind. "Stop finding fault," I told myself. "Accept these people for what they are."

"All right," I agreed. "I will. What they are, no matter what the reason, is a lot of boring, silly, insipid women in Bermudas——"

"But not villains," I reminded myself. "And maybe you wouldn't be so militant against the Bermudas if you didn't have such short legs."

"And maybe you'll mind your own business!" I shot back hotly.

Thinking that if I didn't stop talking to myself, I was liable to wind up as the most celebrated case of schizophrenia this side of Vienna, I did stop talking to myself, until I pulled into our driveway and stopped the car. At that moment, I remembered, "If solid happiness we prize, within our breast this jewel lies and they are fools who roam. The world has nothing to bestow; from our own selves our joys must flow and that dear hut, our home."

"Phooey!" I said. "How far is it from Nathan Cotton to Eddie Guest?"

Tired, I groaned my way out of the car. Glancing around, I noticed that three more daffodils had bloomed in my brief absence, and that the myrtle had put forth a few blue flowers. I saw that Anne was on her terrace, feeding the baby, and gave her a wave—thinking that I could divide some of the myrtle, in the fall, and help my neighbor plant some along her driveway. I looked up at the house and saw how the new white paint sparkled in the sun, and contrasted with the new black paint of the shutters.

191

Then I walked slowly up and onto the terrace, gazed at the house, and said: "You can pick up the marbles now. You win." And the door swung open, the girls shot out, and flung themselves upon me. Planning to greet them with, "Hi! Did you miss me? Did you have a good day?" I was astonished to hear myself saying, instead: "It's true what they say. You can't go home again." But the girls, unsurprised, unbaffled, practical as always, answered:

Louise said: "Of course not, Mommy."

Jennie said: "Because you *are* home."

And Miranda said: "This is where we live. This is home."